Business
Awareness

Workbook

Jo Osborne
Sheriden Amos

Published by Osborne Books Limited
Tel 01905 748071
Email books@osbornebooks.co.uk
Website www.osbornebooks.co.uk

Design by Laura Ingham

Printed by CPI Group (UK) Limited, Croydon, CR0 4YY, on environmentally friendly, acid-free paper from managed forests.

MIX
Paper from responsible sources
FSC® C019777

British Library Cataloguing in Publication Data
A catalogue record for this book is available from the British Library

ISBN 978-1-911198-60-4

Contents

Introduction

Qualifications covered

This book has been written specifically to cover the Unit 'Business Awareness' which is mandatory for the following qualifications:

- AAT Level 3 Diploma in Accounting
- AAT Diploma in Accounting – SCQF Level 7

This book contains Chapter Activities which provide extra practice material in addition to the activities included in the Osborne Books Tutorial text, and Practice Assessments to prepare the student for the computer based assessments. The latter are based directly on the structure, style and content of the sample assessment material provided by the AAT at www.aat.org.uk.

Suggested answers to the Chapter Activities and Practice Assessments are set out in this book.

Osborne Study and Revision Materials

Additional materials, tailored to the needs of students studying this unit and revising for the assessment, include:

- **Tutorials:** paperback books with practice activities
- **Wise Guides:** pocket-sized spiral bound revision cards
- **Student Zone:** access to Osborne Books online resources
- **Osborne Books App:** Osborne Books ebooks for mobiles and tablets

Visit www.osbornebooks.co.uk for details of study and revision resources and access to online material.

Chapter activities

1 Understanding businesses

1.1 **(a)** Explain what is meant by the term 'unlimited liability'.

(b) State two types of business organisation where the liability is limited.

(c) State two types of business organisation where the liability is unlimited.

1.2 For a limited company, tick to indicate which of the following statements are true and which are false.

Statement	True	False
Limited companies are unincorporated business organisations.		
The Articles of Association set out the written rules about running the company.		
The shareholders of a company run it on behalf of the directors.		
Companies follow the accounting rules set out in the Companies Act 2006 and in Financial Reporting Standards.		
The company's Confirmation Statement and Annual Accounts, filed at Companies House, are not available for public inspection.		

1.3 **(a)** Define a limited liability partnership (LLP).

(b) Explain the role of a 'designated member' within an LLP.

1.4 Identify the correct type of business(es) described by each of the statements in the table.

(Some options may be used more than once.)

	Not-for-profit organisation	Public limited company	Partnership (unlimited liability)	Sole trader
If the business becomes insolvent, the assets of the owner(s) may be used to pay the debts of the business.				
Each of the owners of the business will be entitled to a share of the goodwill.				
The rules for running the business are set out in its Articles of Association.				
Must have more than £50,000 of issued share capital.				
Includes charities and public sector organisations.				

1.5 Identify which of the following are common features of business organisations.

Select **two** options.

Individuals working together with a common objective.	
Key responsibility is to shareholders to ensure the organisation generates sufficient profit.	
Owners of the organisation are always involved in the day-to-day operations of the business.	
A group of individuals with defined responsibilities that identify how the work is divided between them.	

1.6 Identify which of the characteristics of a service business is being described by each of the statements below.

Options: intangibility, inseparability, perishability, variability

Any unused service cannot be stored for future use.	
A service will be tailored to the needs of an individual customer or client.	

1.7   Bluebase Ltd is considering the best method of funding a number of different things.

Select the most appropriate funding source for each of the following, using each option only once.

	New capital	Working capital	Loan
Purchase of four new delivery vehicles, which will each cost £32,000, and are expected to last for five years.			
Payment of the business's VAT liability.			
Opening two additional factories, one in Wales and one in Yorkshire.			

1.8   Identify the contribution to the business, and the requirements from the business, for the stakeholders in the table below.

Stakeholder	Contribution to the business	Requirements from the business
Suppliers	Gap1	Gap 2
Professional bodies	Gap 3	Gap 4

Gap 1	
Brand loyalty	
Raw materials	
Capital investment	

Gap 2	
Compliance with regulatory requirements	
Training and development	
Prompt payment of invoices	

Gap 3	
Capital investment	
Payment of fees	
Customer confidence	

Gap 4	
Brand loyalty	
Compliance with ethical codes	
Training and development	

1.9   Complete the following sentences by selecting the correct word for the options available.

Options: risk neutral, risk seeking, risk averse

Sentence	Option
Business stakeholders that try to avoid risk at all costs are ……	
Business stakeholders that look for options that give a higher return for accepting a higher level of risk are……	
Business stakeholders that are willing to accept some risk are ……	

2 Organisational structure and governance

2.1 Decide which organisational structure is best suited to each of the following businesses.

	Functional	Divisional	Matrix
Ready, Steady, Toys Ltd, a toys and games manufacturer. It has two production departments, a sales and marketing team, and departments for finance, administration, and human resources. All of these departments report to the board of directors.			
Albion Ltd, a charity that runs a number of regional outreach projects with a centralised head office function.			
Brentley plc, a car manufacturer, with businesses in different countries all over the world that operate independently, but report to the managing company in the UK.			
Samuels LLP, a firm of solicitors with teams that are responsible for conveyancing, family law, criminal law, and business law.			

2.2 Identify which **one** of the following statements describes a manager with a narrow span of control.

The manager is responsible for a large number of employees doing the same job.	
The manager has a team that is spread across a small geographical area.	
The manager is responsible for a small number of employees.	
The manager has big team, and each person has a very focused role.	

2.3   Decide whether the following statements are true or false.

	True	False
Decisions made at higher levels of the organisation's management indicates decentralised control.		
In a business with centralised control, the higher levels of management will be distanced from the day-to-day running of the business.		
In a business with decentralised control, the lower levels managers are given authority for decision-making.		
The 'top-down' structure of a business with centralised control often leads to a more collaborative working atmosphere.		

2.4   Decide which of the following will normally be responsible for setting the objectives of a business.

Select **one** option.

Employees	
Board of directors	
Shareholders	
Customers	
Suppliers	

2.5   Identify which **two** pieces of information the finance function of a business will receive from the operations function rather than from the sales function.

The price list for items currently sold by the business.	
Overtime hours worked in the week.	
The prices of items bought by the business.	
Discounts negotiated with key customers.	

2.6 Jamingson Ltd has been manufacturing its clothing range in the UK for a number of years but is now considering moving some of its production overseas. It is unclear what the costs of importing and exporting will be if the business decides to go ahead with the move.

Identify what type of risk this presents to the business.

Strategic risk	
Financial risk	
Operational risk	
Cyber risk	

2.7 Identify what is being described by each of the following sentences.

Sentence 1: A cyber-attack that overwhelms the computer systems with a huge number of data requests at the same time, causing the system to freeze.

Sentence 2 A cyber-attack that allows the attacker to watch the operations of the business without being seen by the user.

	Sentence 1	Sentence 2
Malware		
Password attack		
Spyware		
Phishing		
Keylogging		
Distributed denial-of-service attack		

2.8 Identify which of the following is a reputational risk to a business.

Select **one** option.

One of a business's suppliers goes into liquidation.	
The managing director of the business leaves to join a competitor.	
One of its suppliers has been found to be using child workers in its overseas factories.	
The price of one of its competitor's products has been reduced by 20%.	

2.9 Identify which of the following is a financial risk to a business.

Select **one** option.

The business has failed to comply with the ethical code of its professional trade body.	
The human resources director has been signed off for six months due to illness.	
The operations manager has recently made three members of staff redundant as the systems in the business become increasingly automated.	
One of its customers has gone into liquidation, owing the business a substantial amount of money.	

2.10 Decide whether the following statement is true or false.

'A risk matrix is used to evaluate risk in terms of impact and likelihood.'

TRUE/FALSE

2.11 Identify the strategic approach that an organisation could take to manage the following risks.

	Transfer	Accept	Reduce	Avoid
The risk that members of the crowd at a sporting event may need medical assistance.				
The risk that a business will receive high levels of returns from customers due to faults in the manual production process.				

3 The external and internal environment

3.1 Identify which of these is not one of the six categories included in a PESTLE analysis.
Select **one** option.

Technological	
Environmental	
Sustainability	
Legal	

3.2 Identify which of these is not an economic factor in a PESTLE analysis.
Select **one** option.

Inflation	
Public spending	
Changes in disposable income	
Currency exchange rates	

3.3 Identify which of these is an environmental factor in a PESTLE analysis.
Select **one** option.

Changes in technology	
Inflation	
Sustainability	
Consumer protection	

3.4   You have carried out a PESTLE analysis for Stephanie's Sofas and Chairs, a business that manufactures furniture. You have been asked to complete a table showing which PESTLE category certain issues you have identified fall into.

Identify the PESTLE category for each of the issues in the table below. Use each category only once.

	Political	Economic	Social	Techno-logical	Legal	Environ-mental
Import tariffs have been reduced on some of the raw materials required for production.						
Legislation has been introduced that reduces the number of hours delivery drivers are able to work without a break.						
Warehouse staff will use handheld scanners that automatically download despatch notes for customer orders.						
The downturn in the country's economy has led to a decrease in disposable income of the business's customers.						
Due to the downturn in the economy, there are now higher levels of unemployment in the area the business is located, meaning there is a larger population for the business to draw its workforce from.						
One of its suppliers is providing all raw materials in recyclable packaging.						

3.5   This question requires you to produce a PESTLE analysis.

Scenario

Coffee Crescendo is a business that runs a large chain of coffee shops in the UK. The business also imports coffee from Brazil and Colombia, which is sold in supermarkets, as well as in its coffee shops.

The Government is keen to show its 'green' credentials and has placed legal requirements on businesses in the UK to improve their use of recycled materials and reduce the amount of non-recyclable material that is disposed of. Coffee Crescendo currently only recycles a small amount of the waste generated in its coffee shops.

One of the business's employees has suggested that it offers the coffee grounds from its coffee shops to customers for free, as they are known to be very good for gardens.

The significant increase in the cost of gas and electricity has meant that the average household's disposable income has decreased by around 15%.

This increased cost of fuel has also had a negative impact on the delivery costs for Coffee Crescendo. The business uses a delivery company that runs a fleet of diesel vehicles to supply coffee to supermarkets, and to deliver coffee, and other supplies, to the coffee shops that are located across the UK.

From 1 April, the Government is increasing the amount that businesses must contribute to their employees' work-based pensions.

The business currently only uses and sells coffee beans and ground coffee. One of its main competitors has recently started to produce coffee pods which can fit in most coffee machines. Coffee Crescendo does not currently have the necessary production expertise to produce coffee pods.

Customers in the coffee shops are becoming increasingly concerned about the effect of caffeine on their health, and are looking for healthier alternatives.

Coffee Crescendo has used a well-known social media personality to endorse its products. Unfortunately she has recently had some adverse publicity.

The exchange rates between the UK and Brazil and Colombia are unpredictable, which has meant that the business is finding it increasingly difficult to budget for the cost of the coffee it imports.

Although Coffee Crescendo has a website, this does not currently sell its products directly to its customers.

Identify one issue for each of the six PESTLE categories, explain how this may impact the activities of Coffee Crescendo, and what action the business can take to reduce the impact.

Issue	Action
Political	

Economic	

Social	

Technological	

Legal	

Environmental	

3.6   Decide whether each of these statements about business cycles is true or false.

	True	False
In the boom stage of the business cycle unemployment is high.		
In a recession the economy starts to shrink.		
Interest rates are often lowered to stimulate the economy so that it enters the recovery stage.		
When inflation and interest rates start to fall there is likely to be a downturn in the economy.		

3.7   Identify which of the following may cause a shift to the left in the demand curve of a normal good. Select **one** option.

A decrease in the price of a substitute good.	
An increase in the price of a substitute product.	
An increase in the cost of production labour.	
A decrease in the cost of production labour.	

3.8 Identify which of the following may cause a shift along the supply curve of a normal good.
Select **one** option.

A decrease in the price of a substitute good.	
An increase in the price of a substitute product.	
A change in the price of the normal good.	
A change in the price of an inferior good.	

3.9 The following three products are available in the market:
- Doe is a normal good
- Ray is a substitute for Doe
- Mee is a complementary product for Doe

(i) Identify what will happen if the price of Mee decreases.
Select **one** option.

The demand curve for Doe will shift to the left	
The demand curve for Doe will shift to the right	
The demand curve for Doe remains the same	

(ii) Identify what will happen if the price of Ray decreases.
Select **one** option.

An increase in demand for Doe	
A decrease in demand for Doe	
No change in demand for Doe	

3.10   Identify what is defined by each of the statements below by selecting from the following options (use each one once):

Options: Monopoly, Differentiated product, Equilibrium price, Complements

Definition	Option
The point at which supply and demand are equal and the supply and demand curves bisect.	
Goods that must be used together.	
A product that has different features from other, similar products.	
A market with one major supplier who controls most, if not all, of the market.	

3.11   Identify which one of the following is not a barrier to entry, in economic terms.

Select **one** option.

A new restaurant chain that is required to comply with food hygiene requirements.	
A new brand of breakfast cereal entering the market where there is a clear brand leader.	
A frozen food manufacturer with a processing plant close to where the crops are grown.	
An App developer that requires specialist technical expertise that is in short supply.	

4   Sustainability

4.1   **(a)**   State the name of the report that identifies the three key objectives of sustainable development.

(b)   State the three key objectives of sustainability and sustainable development that are set out in this report.

4.2   An increasing number of organisations in the UK are deciding to publish a CSR report.

(a)   State what the abbreviation CSR stands for.

(b)   State what information is normally included in a CSR report.

(c) Give **one** reason why a business might decide to publish a CSR report.

4.3 Byron is a professional accountant who works for Tennyson & Owen, a medium sized accounting practice. His manager, Oswald, has recently returned from an ethics update course run by his professional accounting body. He tells Byron that he must promote an ethics-based culture within Tennyson & Owen and champion sustainability. Byron is not at all sure what Oswald is talking about.

(a) Explain what Oswald means by 'promoting an ethics-based culture' and 'championing sustainability'.

Oswald then goes on to mention the 'triple bottom line', and how important this is to Tennyson & Owen's clients. Byron has no idea what Oswald means but does not want to ask for fear of looking ill-informed.

(b) Explain what Oswald means by 'the triple bottom line' for Tennyson & Owen's clients.

4.4   Simon, the managing director of Gleeson Ltd, has been discussing the performance of the business with his accountant, Ralph. He is very concerned about the possibility that a negative news report is likely to break about Gleeson Ltd's use of child workers in one of its overseas factories. This is likely to adversely affect Gleeson Ltd's reputation.

   (a) State which of the three objectives of sustainability and sustainable development is compromised by the situation that Gleeson Ltd finds itself in.

   (b) Explain what is meant by the term 'reputational risk' and how this is potentially affected by an organisation's attitude to corporate social responsibility.

4.5   Paula is a professional accountant who works in the accounts department of Saunders Supplies Ltd, a business that imports coffee beans and cocoa beans. A number of customers of the business have been asking about the business's 'green' policies. This has prompted the managing director, Ralph, to ask Paula to explain how he might encourage sustainability and sustainable development in the business.

Explain four of the six key areas where Saunders Supplies Ltd should encourage sustainability and sustainable development, and give an example of action that the business can take to support each one.

5 Principles of professional ethics

5.1 Identify the document issued by AAT that provides guidance to full and student members regarding professional ethics.

AAT Rules of Professional Ethics	
AAT Principles of Professional Ethics	
AAT Code of Professional Ethics	

5.2 Identify which of the following is not one of the five fundamental principles of professional ethics.

Select **one** option.

Objectivity	
Confidentiality	
Professional qualification	
Integrity	

5.3 Complete the following sentence by selecting one of the following options.

Options: integrity, objectivity, professional behaviour

When an accountant is faced with a situation that they feel may cause a conflict of interest which could affect their professional judgement, they will have to consider the fundamental ethical principle of [   ] .

5.4 Charlie works for an accounting practice. One of her clients has asked for some detailed inheritance tax advice. The firm does not have any members of staff with the necessary skills to give this advice.

Identify which **one** of these ethical principles is most threatened in this situation.

Professional competence and due care	
Objectivity	
Confidentiality	
Professional behaviour	

5.5   A member of staff has submitted an expense claim for approval. For one client, he has claimed travel expenses for a week when you are certain that he was given a lift in another member of staff's car.

(a)   Decide whether you should process his travel claim.

Yes	No

(b)   Identify which **one** of these ethical principles is most threatened in this situation.

Professional competence and due care	
Objectivity	
Integrity	
Professional behaviour	

5.6   The duty to comply with the five fundamental ethical principles applies to which of the following? Choose **one** option.

Professional accountants in practice	
Professional accountants in business	
Both professional accountants in practice and professional accountants in business	

5.7   List the four key Bribery Act 2010 offences.

5.8   **(a)**   Professional accountants are expected to undertake CPD. What does the abbreviation CPD stand for?

(b)   Decide whether each of these statements is true or false.

	True	False
It is a legal requirement for professional accountants to undertake CPD.		
It is a requirement of the professional accounting bodies for accountants to undertake CPD.		
Carrying out CPD helps an accountant to comply with the ethical principle of professional competence and due care.		

5.9   List the three circumstances in which it is acceptable for a professional accountant to disclose confidential information.

5.10   Vernon is a professional accountant who works for Aston & Fowler, a medium sized firm of accountants. He has just accepted a job offer from Wright & Phipps, another large firm of accountants in the local area.

For each of the following situations, explain whether Vernon can disclose the information requested.

(a)   Vernon's current manager at Aston & Fowler asks Vernon whether he will be paid a higher salary at Wright & Phipps.

(b) Vernon's new manager asks him about the profitability of one of his clients at Aston & Fowler.

(c) Another member of staff at Wright & Phipps asks Vernon to explain how to complete the inheritance tax section of a client's tax return. This is a skill that Vernon learnt whilst working for Aston & Fowler.

5.11 Decide whether the following statement is true or false.

'Professional scepticism means that an accountant must assume everything they are being told is deliberately fraudulent.'

True	False

6 Threats and safeguards to fundamental ethical principles

6.1   State the five types of potential threats to a professional accountant's compliance with the fundamental ethical principles and explain how they may occur.

Type of threat	How this threat may occur

6.2 Leandra is a professional accountant who works for a medium sized firm of accountants. One of her colleagues, Jacob, has recently finished a secondment to the finance department of a client, Hastings Ltd, one of the firm's clients. During her work at Hastings Ltd she reviews the depreciation calculation prepared by Jacob and discovers a significant error in the figures.

(a) State what two types of threat Leandra faces to her fundamental ethical principles.

(b) Explain which three fundamental ethical principles are most threatened by this situation.

6.3 Eugenie has recently been appointed as the finance director of Middlemarch Ltd. Prior to that she was a partner at Windsor & Clarke for fifteen years. Middlemarch Ltd is a client of Windsor & Clarke, and Joel Khan, a manager at Windsor & Clarke, is now about to start an assignment at Middlemarch Ltd.

Explain what type of threat this assignment poses to Joel's fundamental ethical principles.

6.4   Esme is a professional accountant who works in practice. One of her clients, Grow-well Ltd, has recently launched a new product which it claims increases the speed garden plants grow by up to 30%. The managing director of Grow-well Ltd, Jacque, has asked Esme to write a testimonial in the company's new brochure saying what an excellent product it is. He has told her that he's spoken to a friend of his who is a partner in another local accounting practice who says that were Grow-well Ltd his client, he would be happy to write a testimonial for the business.

(a)   State the three threats that Esme faces to her fundamental ethical principles, and briefly explain how they arise.

(b)   If Esme agrees to provide Jacque with the testimonial, explain which of Esme's fundamental ethical principles is most threatened by this situation.

6.5   Moeen is a qualified accountant who works in the finance department of Spragus Ltd. The finance director, Jonathan Rhodes, asks Moeen to come into his office. He explains that Spragus Ltd is shortly to be taken over by a large company and the deal depends on the value of the business being at least £1.5 million. As a consequence he wants Moeen to adjust the depreciation figures on some of the large machinery. He then tells Moeen that he will be part of the management team who decides on redundancies after Spragus Ltd is taken over.

Explain the main threat Moeen is facing to his fundamental ethical principles.

6.6   Pepe works for Ambrose & Harknell, a small firm of accountants. He is currently away on a residential training course for a week. A colleague has taken over his responsibilities while he is away and has found an email from a client marked urgent.

The email is as follows:

Good morning Pepe

Please can you update me on where we are with the bank loan application you were working on for me? I hope you haven't included the fact that I have used my house as security for the business. As we agreed I haven't mentioned any of this to Felix Ambrose and I'm sure you would prefer that I didn't. I will pay you £500 directly into your personal bank account once the loan application has been submitted.

I look forward to hearing from you soon.

Archie Edwards

Managing Director

Edwards Electricals Ltd

(a)   Explain which three of Pepe's fundamental ethical principles are most threatened by the situation detailed in Archie Edwards' email.

| |
| |
| |
| |

(b)   Identify the two types of threats Pepe faces to his fundamental ethical principles.

| |
| |

7 Ethical conflict and reporting unethical behaviour

7.1   Henry works for Catray Ltd, a firm that distributes chemical fertilisers. During the year-end inventory count he identifies 20 bags of poisonous chemicals that are no longer saleable and need to be disposed of. The warehouse manager has said that he will dispose of them 'locally'. Henry is pretty sure that this means the warehouse manager is going to dump the chemicals in a local disused quarry to avoid paying the costs associated with safe disposal. When he raises this with the warehouse manager, he is told that the directors of the business are aware of this plan, and they do not have a problem with it.

(a)   Explain the conflict of loyalties that Henry faces in this situation.

(b)   What options does Henry have to deal with this conflict of loyalties?

7.2 Craig is a qualified professional accountant who works for Andrews & Roberts, a large firm of accountants. The managing director of Andersen Ltd, a client that Craig is working on, has recently contacted him to discuss legal action that it has brought against one of Andersen Ltd's customers, Swann & co. Craig has also received an email from the finance director of Swann & co asking for his professional advice regarding, what appears to be, the same legal case.

(a) Which two of Craig's fundamental ethical principles are threatened by the fact that both Andersen Ltd and Swann & co are both clients of Andrews & Roberts?

(b) What process can Craig go through to resolve the ethical conflict he has in deciding how to deal with this situation?

(c) If Craig decides to act for one of the clients, explain what issues he must consider when carrying out the assignment.

7.3   Becky is a professional accountant who works as a senior manager at Flintoff & Trott, a large accounting practice. One of the partners, Andrea Flintoff, has asked Becky to carry out some management accounting work for a client, Pedro Smith, who is planning to expand his business.

During the course of her work for Pedro, Becky realises that the expansion of the business relies on a large contract which he believes he is about to sign with Greengrass Ltd, another of Flintoff & Trott's clients. She also knows that Greengrass Ltd have some serious concerns over signing the contract with Pedro.

(a)   Explain which two of Becky's fundamental ethical principles are threatened by this situation.

(b)   Identify what steps can Becky take to resolve the ethical conflict that she faces.

7.4 Ryan is a qualified accountant working as a manager in the credit control department of Fischer Ltd. He has just been asked by the finance director to issue a large credit note to one of its customers, Stan Smith. The finance director has not provided Ryan with any supporting documentation for this credit note and Ryan is not aware of anything on Stan Smith's account that would require a credit note. Ryan knows that Stan Smith is a close friend of the finance director, and they regularly play tennis together.

Explain the ethical issues that Ryan faces in this situation, and what he should do to address these.

7.5 Martha Wren is the managing director of Wren Plaster Mouldings Ltd which has recently joined the Plaster Mouldings Trade Association. As part of its membership Martha has received a detailed set of best practice guidelines, which mostly relate to the accounting and payroll functions of the business. She has approached her accountants, Butcher & Evans, for advice on how to implement these guidelines in a code of practice for the company.

List the six key organisational ethical values that Wren Plaster Mouldings Ltd should include in its code of practice.

7.6   **(a)**   Failure by a professional accountant to comply with applicable regulations and codes of practice may result in disciplinary action by which two bodies?

(b)   State the two main categories of misconduct for which a professional accountant may be disciplined.

7.7   Complete the following statement by inserting the correct words in the space.

'Accountants should ensure that they have sufficient [   ] to cover against legal liability to compensate a client who has sustained a loss through a breach in the accountant's duty of care.'

8   Money laundering

8.1   Justine works for a medium sized firm of accountants as an accounting technician. She has been working on the accounts of Simply Scrumptious, an ice-cream restaurant. As part of her work she has spent some time at the client's premises and has noticed that a significant amount of cash is being processed through the business without any supporting paperwork. She is considering raising the issue with the client but doesn't know whether she should raise it with her manager first.

(a)   Explain what offence the client may be committing here.

(b)   Identify which member of staff at the accountant firm Justine should report this issue to.

(c)   Explain what the consequences might be if Justine decides to do nothing in this situation.

(d)   State why Justine should not speak with the client about her concerns before taking any action.

8.2   Maurice is a qualified accountant who works as a sole practitioner. He has recently started work on the year-end accounts for his client Richland Trading Ltd. During his work he discovers a number of payments that have been made to an overseas company that he does not recognise. There is no detailed supporting documentation for these payments. Maurice searches for the company on the internet but only finds a PO Box number for mail deliveries.

Maurice is beginning to suspect that these payments may relate to terrorist activities.

(a)   Explain what Maurice should do in these circumstances.

(b)   Explain the consequences for Maurice of failing to act correctly in this situation.

8.3   State the three key pieces of legislation/regulations that relate to money laundering.

8.4   Briefly explain what each of the three money laundering offences involves.

Concealing
Arrangement
Acquisition

8.5   **(a)**   State the maximum penalties that an individual could face if found guilty of 'failure to report' money laundering or terrorist financing.

(b)   State the name of the document that a sole practitioner should use to report money laundering to the National Crime Agency (NCA).

(c)   State three of the things that must be included in the report identified in **(b)**.

8.6 Niamh is a qualified accountant who works for Harding & Hadley, an accounting practice in Dealborough. She has just agreed, in principle, to take on a new client, Lucinda Smyth, who runs a successful catering business in Dealborough. Lucinda's husband, Monty, is also a partner in the business, although he does not take an active part in running it. Although Niamh has met Lucinda socially, she has never dealt with her husband.

State the customer due diligence (CDD) procedures that Niamh should carry out before she can take Lucinda on as a client.

8.7 Noah is an accountant who works for a medium sized firm of accountants. He is currently completing some tax work for his client Maya. He has just realised that Maya owes HMRC a substantial sum of money for income tax on share dividends that she did not declare on her previous year's tax return.

When Noah raises this with Maya, she refuses to declare the income, saying that she has recently received a letter from HMRC confirming that it has agreed her previous year's return so she does not see why she should have to pay it the tax Noah says she owes.

(a) Explain what Noah must do in this situation.

(b)   What are the consequences for Noah if he does not take any action in this situation?

9   New technology and data security

9.1   Decide whether each of the following sentences is true or false.

	True	False
Using automatic intelligence increases the chance of human error.		
Automatic intelligence and machine learning will speed up data entry.		
Bespoke automatic intelligence and machine learning is cheap and available to all sizes of business.		

9.2   Identify what is being described here.

'An application of artificial intelligence that is not explicitly programmed. Instead, it bases its actions on past events to predict the probability of what will happen next.'

Select **one** option.

Data analytics	
Blockchain	
Machine learning	

9.3   Complete the following sentences by selecting the correct words from the following options.

Options: secure and confidential; paper-based and readable; quick and efficient.

The advantage to the finance function of using electronic signatures is that it is [   ].

However, the business must be confident that the documents remain [   ].

9.4   Identify which category of data analytics can be used to find out what has caused something that has happened.

Select **one** option.

Descriptive	
Diagnostic	
Predictive	
Prescriptive	

9.5   Identify which category of data analytics uses machine learning and algorithms to make recommendations for problem solving.

Select **one** option.

Descriptive	
Diagnostic	
Predictive	
Prescriptive	

9.6   Premalta Ltd is a large insurance business located in the UK. It has decided to relocate its customer services team for motor insurance to India.

Decide whether each of the following statements is true or false.

	True	False
This is an example of Premalta Ltd offshoring its motor insurance customer services function.		
This is an example of Premalta Ltd outsourcing its motor insurance customer services function.		
In the first year after this change Premalta Ltd can expect to save money.		
The key benefit Premalta Ltd is likely to get from this move is reduced costs.		
Premalta Ltd may have to overcome cultural or language issues as a result of this move.		

9.7   Identify which of these are advantages of cloud accounting.

Select **all** options that apply.

Data is updated whenever a backup is created.	
Data and information can be accessed remotely from anywhere.	
Improved sustainability, as more documents are stored electronically.	
Data is stored more securely.	
Cloud accounting software relies on internet access.	

9.8   Identify which of the following are valid statements about data protection.

Select **all** options that apply.

Once a business has finished with personal data it must store it securely.	
Data should only be used for the explicit purpose for which it was given.	
Failure to comply with data protection legislation may result in a fine.	
A business must keep personal data that it holds secure from internal and external threats.	
Businesses must have appropriate measures and records in place to prove they are complying with data protection principles.	
Personal data held by a business must be updated every month.	

9.9   State the three types of integrity controls a business can use to ensure data it holds is complete and accurate.

9.10   Complete each of the follow sentences about cyberattacks.

(a)   [   ] is a cyberattack that sends a message to a user in an attempt to trick

them into opening an email or an attachment that will attack the system.

(b)   [   ] is a virus that allows the attacker to record the keystrokes the user

makes, and then recreates these strokes to identify passwords, or other sensitive information.

9.11   Identify which of the cyber security measures each of the descriptions relates to.

	Data encryption	Antivirus software
Once installed on a computer system, it runs in the background, providing real-time protection against cyberattacks.		
Software that translates data into another form or code that only authorised users, with the necessary password, can read.		

| 10 | Communicating information to stakeholders |

10.1 Identify which of these are not attributes of good quality information.

Select **all** that apply.

Understandable	
Timely	
Authoritative	
Evaluated	
Cost effective	
Efficient	

10.2 Gita, the finance manager, produces a monthly profitability report for the board of directors on 4th of each month. She suggests that the directors raise any queries they have before the monthly board meeting which is held around 12th of the month.

Complete the two sentences below by selecting the correct quality of good information from these options.

Options: cost effective, relevant, timely, easy to use, authoritative.

'The fact that Gita, a qualified accountant who has been the finance manager at the business for three years, produces the report will help to ensure that the information is [   ].'

'Because the report is produced on 4th of each month and the board meeting is a week later, this helps to ensure that the information is [   ].'

10.3   Decide whether each of these statements about information provided at different levels of an organisation is true or false.

	True	False
Information provided at the strategic level of an organisation will be detailed rather than summarised.		
Information at the management level will be used to translate the strategic goals of an organisation into practical plans.		
Information provided at the strategic level of a business is used to support longer term decisions for the future.		
Information provided at the operational level will be summarised rather than detailed.		
Information used at the management level of an organisation will be mostly generated internally.		

10.4   Briefly explain what is meant by transactional data as a source of big data.

10.5   Identify which of these is not a characteristic of big data.

Select **one** option.

Volume	
Velocity	
Veracity	
Validity	

10.6   List **three** of the benefits of using big data.

| |
| |
| |

10.7   Decide whether the following statement is true or false.

'If big data has been analysed by an external source, there is no requirement for an accountant to apply professional scepticism.'

True	False

10.8   Nazreen is preparing some information for a presentation to the senior management team at Dorsey Ltd, a business that sells computer games. She is keen to use a variety of different methods to present the information.

Match each of the following pieces of information to the most appropriate presentation method, using each option once.

A flowchart detailing the revised process for staff expenses claims.	Table
Monthly profit or loss for the last six months.	Pie chart
The split of the total customers by age.	Diagram
The seasonal movement in sales over a 12 month period.	Line graph

10.9 Simplon Ltd, a business that makes small household appliances, has recently recruited a new HR manager who has identified weaknesses in the organisation's communication with its stakeholders.

For each of the following stakeholders, identify which is the most appropriate method of communication.

	Email	Meeting	Social media	Intranet	Report
Detailed information about the business's results to support an application for a bank loan.					
To provide a signed contract to a new supplier.					
To present the features of new products to the staff at a large customer.					
To offer a 25% discount code for anyone ordering by midnight.					

10.10 Ashley's Accessories Ltd is a business owned by Ashley Andrews that sells accessories, including scarves, hats, and gloves. Ashley started the business five years ago as a hobby, selling accessories at craft fairs and markets. The business has grown since then, and Ashley now employs three members of staff who deal with customers, suppliers, and the administration of the business, and one person who deals with despatch from the warehouse.

The range of products sold by the business includes tote bags, scarves, gloves, hats, and socks.

Most sales are made to independent retailers that sell the products in their shops. However, the business also has a website where it sells directly to customers.

In March the business had an end of season sale.

In the middle of April one of the overseas suppliers that Ashley's Accessories buys from contacted her to say that the shipment of summer scarves that were due to be delivered at the end of April had been delayed and will not now arrive until June.

The business uses a cloud accounting package to record its sales and purchases which the external accountants use at the end of the year to produce the financial statements.

Ashley knows that the accounting package currently produces a standard sales dashboard that shows key information, but she has not used this information to date.

The latest sales dashboard for the first three months of the financial year is shown on the next page.

Bank Balances		Upcoming transactions:	
Petty cash	£114.00	-£9,475.00	Wages BACS
Current Account	£27,451.22	-£150.00	Cash withdrawal
Deposit Account	£124,550.00	-£3,200.00	J Johnstones - Monthly rent
		+£2,740.50	Destanto ltd

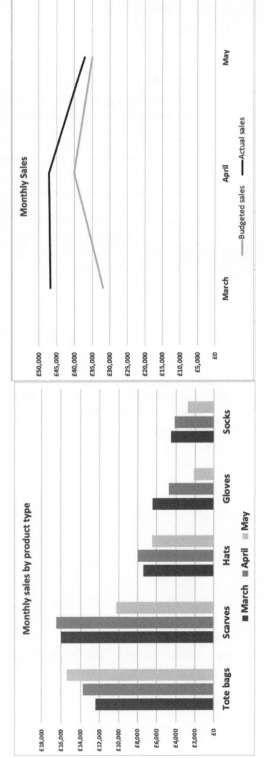

Monthly Sales

— Budgeted sales — Actual sales

Monthly sales by product type

■ March ■ April ■ May

Tote bags · Scarves · Hats · Gloves · Socks

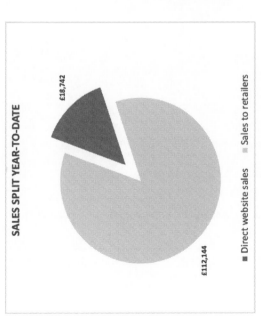

SALES SPLIT YEAR-TO-DATE

£18,742

£112,144

■ Direct website sales ■ Sales to retailers

Ashley has asked you the following questions about the dashboard that is produced by the accounting package.

1.   Why does the supplier of the accounting software say that the dashboard can be a useful tool for owners of a business?

2.   Can you briefly explain to me what the key messages are from the data in the standard dashboard?

3.   Is there anything you think is missing from the dashboard that might help me to better understand how the business is doing?

(a)   Explain three benefits of using a dashboard to present financial information to stakeholders in a business.

(b)   Explain three conclusions you can draw about the performance of the business from the data shown in the dashboard.

(c)   State one thing that might be useful to Ashley to improve her understanding of the performance of the business.

10.11 It is 12pm and Joel, the sales manager, has called a meeting of all eight members of the sales team at 12.30pm. He has not issued an agenda for the meeting. Some of the sales staff are out visiting customers, and those that are in the office are anxious about what the meeting might be about.

From the list below, identify the **two** issues that have arisen in the communication process in this situation.

Misunderstanding	
Negative body language	
Information overload	
Lack of planning	

Answers to chapter activities

1 Understanding businesses

1.1 **(a)** Where a business has unlimited liability, this means that should it become insolvent, the personal assets of the owner(s) may be used to pay the debts of the business.

(b) limited liability partnerships (LLPs)

limited companies

(c) sole traders

partnerships

1.2

Statement	True	False
Limited companies are unincorporated business organisations.		✔
The Articles of Association set out the written rules about running the company.	✔	
The shareholders of a company run it on behalf of the directors.		✔
Companies follow the accounting rules set out in the Companies Act 2006 and in Financial Reporting Standards.	✔	
The company's Confirmation Statement and Annual Accounts, filed at Companies House, are not available for public inspection.		✔

1.3 **(a)** A limited liability partnership is an incorporated form of partnership, which is a separate legal entity from its owners, where members are able to limit their personal liability for the debts of the business.

(b) A 'designated member' of an LLP is responsible for ensuring that the legal and accounting requirements are carried out, eg keeping accounting records, arranging for the accounts to be audited if required, preparing, and submitting the LLP's Confirmation Statement and Annual Accounts to Companies House.

1.4

	Not-for-profit organisation	Public limited company	Partnership (unlimited liability)	Sole trader
If the business becomes insolvent, the assets of the owner(s) may be used to pay the debts of the business.			✔	✔
Each of the owners of the business will be entitled to a share of the goodwill.			✔	
The rules for running the business are set out in its Articles of Association.		✔		
Must have more than £50,000 of issued share capital.		✔		
Includes charities and public sector organisations.	✔			

1.5

Individuals working together with a common objective.	✔
Key responsibility is to shareholders to ensure the organisation generates sufficient profit.	
Owners of the organisation are always involved in the day-to-day operations of the business.	
A group of individuals with defined responsibilities that identify how the work is divided between them.	✔

1.6

Any unused service cannot be stored for future use.	perishability
A service will be tailored to the needs of an individual customer or client.	variability

1.7

	New capital	Working capital	Loan
Purchase of four new delivery vehicles, which will each cost £32,000, and are expected to last for five years.			✔
Payment of the business's VAT liability.		✔	
Opening two additional factories, one in Wales and one in Yorkshire.	✔		

1.8

Stakeholder	Contribution to the business	Requirements from the business
Suppliers	Raw materials	Prompt payment of invoice
Professional bodies	Customer confidence	Compliance with ethical codes

1.9

Sentence	Option
Business stakeholders that try to avoid risk at all costs are ……	Risk adverse
Business stakeholders that look for options that give a higher return for accepting a higher level of risk are……	Risk seeking
Business stakeholders that are willing to accept some risk are……	Risk neutral

2   Organisational structure and governance

2.1

	Functional	Divisional	Matrix
Ready, Steady, Toys Ltd, a toys and games manufacturer. It has two production departments, a sales and marketing team, and departments for finance, administration, and human resources. All of these departments report to the board of directors.	✔		
Albion Ltd, a charity that runs a number of regional outreach projects with a centralised head office function.			✔
Brentley plc, a car manufacturer, with businesses in different countries all over the world that operate independently, but report to the managing company in the UK.		✔	
Samuels LLP, a firm of solicitors with teams that are responsible for conveyancing, family law, criminal law, and business law.		✔	

2.2

The manager is responsible for a large number of employees doing the same job.	
The manager has a team that is spread across a small geographical area.	
The manager is responsible for a small number of employees.	✔
The manager has big team, and each person has a very focused role.	

2.3

	True	False
Decisions made at higher levels of the organisation's management indicates decentralised control.		✔
In a business with centralised control, the higher levels of management will be distanced from the day-to-day running of the business.	✔	
In a business with decentralised control, the lower levels managers are given authority for decision-making.	✔	
The 'top-down' structure of a business with centralised control often leads to a more collaborative working atmosphere.		✔

2.4

Employees	
Board of directors	✔
Shareholders	
Customers	
Suppliers	

2.5

The price list for items currently sold by the business.	
Overtime hours worked in the week.	✔
The prices of items bought by the business.	✔
Discounts negotiated with key customers.	

2.6

Strategic risk	✔
Financial risk	
Operational risk	
Cyber risk	

2.7

	Sentence 1	Sentence 2
Malware		
Password attack		
Spyware		✔
Phishing		
Keylogging		
Distributed denial-of-service attack	✔	

2.8

One of a business's suppliers goes into liquidation.	
The managing director of the business leaves to join a competitor.	
One of its suppliers has been found to be using child workers in its overseas factories.	✔
The price of one of its competitor's products has been reduced by 20%.	

2.9

The business has failed to comply with the ethical code of its professional trade body.	
The human resources director has been signed off for six months due to illness.	
The operations manager has recently made three members of staff redundant as the systems in the business become increasingly automated.	
One of its customers has gone into liquidation, owing the business a substantial amount of money.	✔

2.10   True. A risk matrix is used to evaluate risk in terms of impact and likelihood.

2.11

	Transfer	Accept	Reduce	Avoid
The risk that members of the crowd at a sporting event may need medical assistance			✔	
The risk that a business will receive high levels of returns from customers due to faults in the manual production process.				✔

3 The external and internal environment

3.1

Technological	
Environmental	
Sustainability	✔
Legal	

3.2

Inflation	
Public spending	✔
Changes in disposable income	
Currency exchange rates	

3.3

Changes in technology	
Inflation	
Sustainability	✔
Consumer protection	

3.4

	Political	Economic	Social	Techno-logical	Legal	Environ-mental
Import tariffs have been reduced on some of the raw materials required for production.	✔					
Legislation has been introduced that reduces the number of hours delivery drivers are able to work without a break.					✔	
Warehouse staff will use handheld scanners that automatically download despatch notes for customer orders.				✔		
The downturn in the country's economy has led to a decrease in disposable income of the business's customers.		✔				
Due to the downturn in the economy, there are now higher levels of unemployment in the area the business is located, meaning there is a larger population for the business to draw its workforce from.			✔			
One of its suppliers is providing all raw materials in recyclable packaging.						✔

3.5

Issue	Action
Political The Government's focus on the environment, including legislation to improve the use of recycled materials and reduce the amount of non-recyclable materials used, means that Coffee Crescendo will have to improve its green credentials.	Introduce a discount for coffee shop customers who bring their own reusable cup. Investigate offering coffee grounds to customers for their gardens rather than disposing of them as waste. Try and source recyclable coffee cups.
Economic Unpredictable exchange rates have meant that it is difficult to budget for the actual price that will be paid for coffee imported from Brazil and Colombia. This may have a negative impact on the business's profits.	Coffee Crescendo could negotiate prices in UK £s with its overseas suppliers. The business may have to consider increasing prices to ensure that it maintains margins, although this may not be effective given the reduction in disposable income due to increases in the cost of customers' gas and electricity.
Social Coffee shop customers are looking for healthier alternatives rather than simply coffee. The adverse publicity that the social media personality has had may have a negative effect on the popularity of the Coffee Crescendo products.	The business should consider offering decaffeinated coffee, and other non-caffeine based drinks, to cater for changes in customer tastes. Coffee Crescendo should try and distance itself from the social media personality and find an alternative way of advertising its products.
Technological Coffee Crescendo does not currently have a website where customers can buy directly. This may mean that it is missing out on potential sales. A competitor is now producing its coffee in pods which can be used in most coffee machines. This may lead to loss of supermarket sales for the business.	The business should investigate updating its website so that it can sell directly to customers. Coffee Crescendo should consider producing coffee pods that it can offer to supermarkets as an alternative to coffee beans, or ground coffee.
Legal The legal requirement to use more recycled material and reduce the amount of non-recyclable material that businesses disposed of may result in further costs for the business.	As detailed in the political section above, the business should consider: Introducing a discount for customers with reusable cups. Offer coffee grounds to customers rather than disposing of them as waste. Try and source recyclable coffee cups.

The increased contribution to work-based pensions will increase the costs of the business.	Both of these legal factors mean that the business may have to consider increasing prices to ensure that it maintains margins. However, this may reduce sales given the reduction in disposable income due to increases in the cost of customers' gas and electricity.
Environmental Coffee Crescendo currently only recycles a small amount of the waste generated in its coffee shops.	As stated in the political section above, Coffee Crescendo should investigate offering coffee grounds to customers for their gardens rather than disposing of them. It should also investigate recyclable options for the cups, and other products it uses.
The delivery company that Coffee Crescendo uses runs a fleet of diesel vehicles which causes damage to the environment.	The business should consider alternative, more environmentally friendly delivery options.

3.6

	True	False
In the boom stage of the business cycle unemployment is high.		✔
In a recession the economy starts to shrink.	✔	
Interest rates are often lowered to stimulate the economy so that it enters the recovery stage.	✔	
When inflation and interest rates start to fall there is likely to be a downturn in the economy.		✔

3.7

A decrease in the price of a substitute good.	✔
An increase in the price of a substitute product.	
An increase in the cost of production labour.	
A decrease in the cost of production labour.	

3.8

A decrease in the price of a substitute good.	
An increase in the price of a substitute product.	
A change in the price of the normal good.	✔
A change in the price an inferior good.	

3.9   **(i)**

The demand curve for Doe will shift to the left	
The demand curve for Doe will shift to the right	✔
The demand curve for Doe remains the same	

(ii)

An increase in demand for Doe	
A decrease in demand for Doe	✔
No change in demand for Doe	

3.10

Definition	Option
The point at which supply and demand are equal and the supply and demand curves bisect.	Equilibrium price
Goods that must be used together.	Complements
A product that has different features from other, similar products.	Differentiated product
A market with one major supplier who controls most, if not all, of the market.	Monopoly

3.11

A new restaurant chain that is required to comply with food hygiene requirements.	
A new brand of breakfast cereal entering the market where there is a clear brand leader.	
A frozen food manufacturer with a processing plant close to where the crops are grown.	✔
An App developer that requires specialist technical expertise that is in short supply.	

4   Sustainability

4.1   **(a)**

The Brundtland Report

(b)

Economic growth
Environmental protection
Social equality

4.2   **(a)**

Corporate social responsibility

(b)

A CSR report details how the organisation takes responsibility for supporting sustainable development through the way in which it operates and its policies and procedures. It also measures to what extent it has achieved its CSR objectives.

(c)

The public and investors are keen to see a business's attitude to sustainability and will look more favourably on organisations which have made progress towards achieving their CSR goals.

4.3   **(a)**

Professional accountants must act ethically in all aspects of their working life and in addition to this, should actively encourage and promote an ethics-based culture that discourages unethical or illegal practices.
Sustainability inherently relies on the management of an organisation acting in an ethical manner. It focuses on achieving the business's current aims without jeopardising its long term needs.
Accountants should support (champion) sustainability. However, they must also remain objective and give equal consideration to all relevant issues before making an ethical decision.

(b)

> The 'triple bottom line' refers to the three objectives of the Brundtland report. Oswald means that Tennyson & Owen and its staff should take social, environmental, and financial, or economic, factors into account when measuring the position and performance of its clients and when assisting with their decision-making.

4.4   **(a)**

> Social equality

(b)

> Reputational risk is the risk of loss resulting from damage to an organisation's reputation. An organisation will include its sustainability targets in its corporate social responsibility (CSR) objectives. When it produces a CSR report, this will show its progress towards these targets.
>
> There is a risk to an organisation's reputation if it reports negative results. However, the fact that a business is prepared to report its progress towards its sustainability targets and CSR will have a positive effect on its reputation.

4.5   Answer should include four of the six key areas below.

Products and services – Saunders Supplies Ltd should ensure that its products or services are produced from sustainably resourced materials. *example* – Saunders Supplies Ltd imports coffee beans and cocoa beans; it should investigate where these products are grown to ensure that the farming methods do not damage the environment, for example by deforestation.
Customers – Saunders Supplies Ltd should ensure that it supplies to its customers in a sustainable manner. *example* – this could be by using recycled packaging material, or through environmentally friendly delivery methods such as lower carbon emission vehicles.
Employees – Saunders Supplies Ltd should encourage good working conditions for its staff and encourage its staff to take appropriate qualifications if they wish. *example* – all members of the accounts department should be offered the opportunity to enrol on accounting courses which should be part or fully funded by the business.
The workplace – Saunders Supplies Ltd should introduce environmentally friendly initiatives in the workplace. *example* – introduce recycling policies in the offices, encourage conservation of energy and then monitor the participation of staff in the schemes to measure their success.
The supply chain – Saunders Supplies Ltd should source its coffee and cocoa beans from ethically responsible suppliers. *example* – Saunders Supplies Ltd should buy coffee and cocoa beans that have the Fairtrade certification. This demonstrates that farmers producing the coffee and cocoa have been paid a reasonable price for their products.
Business functions and processes – Saunders Supplies Ltd must regularly review the way in which it operates to ensure it continues to support and encourage sustainability and sustainable development. *example* – for each of the points 1-5 above, Saunders Supplies Ltd should carry out regular reviews and measure the extent to which the business is achieving its sustainability targets.

5 Principles of professional ethics

5.1

AAT Rules of Professional Ethics	
AAT Principles of Professional Ethics	
AAT Code of Professional Ethics	✔

5.2

Objectivity	
Confidentiality	
Professional qualification	✔
Integrity	

5.3 When an accountant is faced with a situation that they feel may cause a conflict of interest which could affect their professional judgement, they will have to consider the fundamental ethical principle of **objectivity**.

5.4

Professional competence and due care	✔
Objectivity	
Confidentiality	
Professional behaviour	

5.5 **(a)** No, you should not process his travel claim without further investigation.

(b)

Professional competence and due care	
Objectivity	
Integrity	✔
Professional behaviour	

5.6

Professional accountants in practice	
Professional accountants in business	
Both professional accountants in practice and professional accountants in business	✔

5.7

Bribing another
Receiving a bribe
Bribing a foreign official
Failure to prevent bribery

5.8 **(a)**

Continuing Professional Development

(b)

	True	False
It is a legal requirement for professional accountants to undertake CPD.		✔
It is a requirement of the professional accounting bodies for accountants to undertake CPD.	✔	
Carrying out CPD helps an accountant to comply with the ethical principle of professional competence and due care.	✔	

5.9

When authorised by a client or employer.
When disclosure is required by law.
Where there is a professional duty to disclose.

5.10 **(a)**

> This information is personal to Vernon, so unless he has been specifically asked by the management of Wright & Phipps not to disclose it, Vernon can choose whether he tells his current manager about the salary he will be paid by Wright & Phipps.

(b)

> Vernon has a duty of confidentiality to his clients that extends after the relationship has ended. This means he cannot disclose this information to his new manager.

(c)

> Vernon is allowed to use general knowledge and experience gained from previous employment, but not specific information that is covered by his duty of confidentiality to the employer or its clients. This means he can explain how to complete the inheritance tax section of a client's tax return to his new colleague.

5.11 False. Professional scepticism means that an accountant should be alert to things that might indicate possible misstatement due to error or fraud.

6 Threats and safeguards to fundamental ethical principles

6.1

Type of threat	How this threat may occur
Self-interest threat	This type of threat may occur where a financial, or other interest, may inappropriately influence an accountant's judgment or behaviour.
Self-review threat	This type of threat may occur when work carried out by an accountant has to be re-evaluated by the accountant at a later date.
Advocacy threat	This type of threat may occur when an accountant goes beyond an advisory role by publicly supporting a client in some way.
Familiarity threat	This type of threat may occur when there is a family relationship or close friendship between an accountant and their client, supplier customer, work colleague or manager.
Intimidation threat	This type of threat, whether real or perceived, may occur when a client exerts undue pressure on an accountant in practice, or a dominant employer, or manager, attempts to influence an accountant in business.

6.2   **(a)**

Self-review threat (Leandra is reviewing work that has been produced by Jacob who works for the same firm as she does.)
Self-interest threat (as Leandra is reviewing work that has been produced by another member of staff at the firm she works for, she is facing a self-interest threat. Highlighting Jacob's error could make her firm's staff look incompetent and jeopardise the future relationship with Hastings Ltd. This also represents a self-interest threat as the loss of the client would have a direct impact on the firm's fee income.)

(b)

Objectivity – the self-interest threat will affect Leandra's objectivity.
Professional competence and due care – if Leandra does not report Jacob's error this would be a lack of professional competence and due care on the part of her firm.
Professional behaviour – if Leandra is aware of the error that Jacob has made, her failure to report the error would be considered unprofessional behaviour.

6.3

> This is a familiarity threat to Joel's fundamental principles due to the close relationship that Eugenie previously had with the staff at Windsor & Clarke and the fact that she is now in a position of significant influence at Middlemarch Ltd.

6.4   **(a)**

> Advocacy threat – if Esme agrees to provide the testimonial for Grow-well Ltd, she would be supporting the client and so would be facing an advocacy threat to her fundamental ethical principles.

> Intimidation threat – the managing director is putting pressure on Esme to provide his business with the testimonial.

> Self-interest threat – the managing director is giving a strong indication that if Esme does not give Grow-well Ltd the testimonial, he may dismiss her as its accountant and employ his friend's firm.

   (b)

> If Esme agrees to provide Jacque with the testimonial, her independence and hence objectivity will be most threatened.

6.5

> Intimidation threat – the finance director is attempting to influence Moeen's behaviour and is also suggesting that he may be made redundant if he does not comply with his wishes.

6.6   **(a)**

> Integrity – omitting the fact that Archie has used his house as security for the business means that Pepe is involved with providing misleading information, which is dishonest.

> Objectivity – the offer of payment from Archie represents undue pressure, which may affect Pepe's professional judgement.

> Professional behaviour – submitting misleading information to the bank is dishonest and therefore brings the accounting profession into disrepute.

   (b)

> Intimidation threat – Pepe faces an intimidation threat from Archie as he is suggesting he may tell his employers if he does not do as he asks.

> Self-interest threat – Pepe faces a self-interest threat from the offer of £500 for completing the loan application.

7 Ethical conflict and reporting unethical behaviour

7.1   **(a)**

Henry is employed by Catray Ltd and therefore is expected to be loyal to his employer; however, he also has a duty of loyalty to his profession. The business is acting illegally by dumping the chemicals and not disposing of them safely. This is contrary to Henry's fundamental ethical principles of integrity and professional behaviour.

(b)

He should try to resolve the difference of opinion with the warehouse manager. Despite the warehouse manager saying the directors are happy with this behaviour, Henry should raise this issue with a more senior member of staff at Catray Ltd and try to persuade them not to act illegally. If Catray Ltd has a formal dispute resolution process, Henry should consider using this to escalate the issue. Henry can also consult with his professional accounting body and take legal advice. Ultimately, if there are no other options open to Henry, he may have to offer to resign from Catray Ltd.

7.2   **(a)**

Objectivity – giving advice to both clients when they are in a legal dispute would be very difficult for Craig. Even if he manages to remain independent, it could appear to each of the two clients that he is favouring the other.

Confidentiality – it will be difficult for Craig to keep information about each client confidential. Again, each client may perceive that he will use confidential information about it to benefit the other.

(b)

- Consider the relevant facts and ethical issues that this situation raises.

- Establish whether Andrews & Roberts has a set procedure for dealing with conflicts of interest between clients.

- Decide what alternative courses of action are available to him.

- Select the course of action that is most consistent with his fundamental principles.

- Discuss the issue with senior management at Andrews & Roberts and document the issue and the discussion.

(c)

> It is very unlikely that the threats to Craig's fundamental ethical principles can be eliminated, or reduced to an acceptable level, so that he can act for one of these clients.
>
> However, if he decides that he can act for one of them, he must consider what safeguards he can put in place so that his relationship with the other client does not affect his professional judgement and his objectivity. These safeguards must also ensure that he does not breach the confidentiality of the other client.

7.3   **(a)**

> Confidentiality – Becky must be careful not to use confidential information gained from her work with Greengrass Ltd to advise Pedro.

> Professional competence and due care – due care is the key issue in this situation; Becky does not want to compromise her professional competence and due care by failing to advise Pedro about the risks of relying on the contract with Greengrass Ltd.

(b)

> - Gather all the relevant facts.
> - Assess the ethical issues that this situation raises.
> - Consider whether Flintoff & Trott has an established procedure (formal or informal) for the resolution of ethical conflicts; this may include reporting the issue to a more senior member of staff, probably Andrea Flintoff.
> - Decide what alternative courses of action are available to her. This could involve explaining to Pedro that Flintoff & Trott already acts for Greengrass Ltd, and that its professional competence and due care, and confidentiality, could be compromised if it continues to act for him.
> - Formally discuss the issue with senior management at Flintoff & Trott and document the issue and the discussion.

7.4

> Ryan appears to have identified possible unethical behaviour on the part of the finance director as there seems to be no valid reason for issuing Stan Smith with a credit note. This puts Ryan in a difficult position due to the senior position that the finance director holds at Fischer Ltd. Ryan should gather together all the information relating to the credit note and present it to another director of the business explaining his concerns regarding the situation. If the other director does not deal with the situation, Ryan should then consider taking advice from his professional accounting body as to what further action he should take.
>
> In this situation Ryan should not simply process the credit note as this would be contrary to his fundamental ethical principles.

7.5

Being transparent with colleagues, customers, and suppliers.
Reporting financial and regulatory information clearly and on time.
Being open and honest by identifying when it is appropriate to accept and give gifts and hospitality.
Paying suppliers a fair price and on time.
Providing fair treatment, decent wages, and good working conditions for employees.
Appropriate use of social media.

7.6   **(a)**

The individual accountant's professional accounting body.
The Financial Reporting Council (FRC).

(b)

Bringing the accounting profession into disrepute.
Acting in breach of the rules and regulations of the accountant's professional body.

7.7   'Accountants should ensure that they have sufficient **professional indemnity insurance** to cover against legal liability to compensate a client who has sustained a loss through a breach in the accountant's duty of care.'

8 Money laundering

8.1 **(a)**

> The client may be committing money laundering by processing criminally obtained funds through the accounts of the business.

(b)

> Justine should report her concerns to the Money Laundering Reporting Officer (MLRO) at the firm where she works. They will assess the issue and decide whether to report the matter to the National Crime Agency.

(c)

> Justine may be guilty of failure to disclose.

(d)

> This would be tipping off – a money laundering offence that carries a penalty of five years imprisonment and/or a fine.

8.2 **(a)**

> As Maurice is a sole practitioner, he will not have a Money Laundering Reporting Officer (MLRO) to whom he can report his concerns. He should, therefore, report his concerns to the National Crime Agency (NCA) using a Suspicious Activity Report (SAR).

(b)

> Failure to do this could result in Maurice himself being charged with terrorist financing offences. He should not inform anyone at Richland Trading Ltd of his suspicions.

8.3

> The Proceeds of Crime Act 2002
>
> The Terrorism Act 2000
>
> The Money Laundering and Terrorist Financing Regulations 2020

8.4

Concealing
A person commits the money laundering offence of concealing if they conceal, disguise, convert, or transfer criminal property, or remove it from the UK.
Arrangement
A person may be guilty of the money laundering offence of arrangement if they enter into, or become concerned in an arrangement with another person, which they know involves criminal property.
Acquisition
A person may be guilty of the money laundering offence of acquisition if they acquire, use, or have possession of criminal property.

8.5   **(a)**

Up to five years imprisonment and/or a fine.

(b)

Suspicious Activity Report (SAR).

(c)   Any three of the following:

The identity of the suspected person (if known) including full name, address, telephone numbers, passport details, date of birth, account details.
Information on which the suspicion of money laundering is based.
The whereabouts of the laundered property, if it is known.
Details of the person making the SAR; this will normally be the Money Laundering Reporting Officer (MLRO) or sole practitioner.

8.6

Niamh should verify Lucinda's identity by looking at documents, data or other information obtained from a reliable source, eg her passport.
Niamh should ensure that she fully understands who the beneficial owners of the business are – in this case Lucinda's husband, Monty. She should also verify Monty's identity.
Niamh should find out what Lucinda wants from the professional relationship with her (in practice this will have been discussed prior to Niamh agreeing to take Lucinda on as a client).
Niamh must ensure that she keeps written documentation of the CDD that she carries out for Lucinda and Monty.

8.7 **(a)**

> Noah must tell Maya that he can no longer act for her. This is because the money that she has not paid to HMRC constitutes criminal property and, by retaining it, Maya could be charged with money laundering. Noah must not tell Maya why he can no longer act for her as this could constitute 'tipping off' which may prejudice a money laundering investigation. As Noah works for a medium sized firm of accountants, he must make an internal report to the Money Laundering Reporting Officer (MLRO) who will then submit a Suspicious Activity Report (SAR) to the National Crime Agency (NCA).

(b)

> If Noah continues to act for Maya, then he is facilitating her retention of the money she should have paid to HMRC. In this situation Noah could also be accused of money laundering. He may also be guilty of the crime of failure to disclose.

9 | New technology and data security

9.1

	True	False
Using automatic intelligence increases the chance of human error.		✔
Automatic intelligence and machine learning will speed up data entry.	✔	
Bespoke, automatic intelligence and machine learning is cheap and available to all sizes of business.		✔

9.2

Data analytics	
Blockchain	
Machine learning	✔

9.3 The advantage to the finance function of using electronic signatures is that it is **quick and efficient**. However, the business must be confident that the documents remain **secure and confidential**.

9.4

Descriptive	
Diagnostic	✔
Predictive	
Prescriptive	

9.5

Descriptive	
Diagnostic	
Predictive	
Prescriptive	✔

9.6

	True	False
This is an example of Premalta Ltd offshoring its motor insurance customer services function.	✔	
This is an example of Premalta Ltd outsourcing its motor insurance customer services function.		✔
In the first year after this change Premalta Ltd can expect to save money.		✔
The key benefit Premalta Ltd is likely to get from this move is reduced costs.	✔	
Premalta Ltd may have to overcome cultural or language issues as a result of this move.	✔	

9.7

Data is updated whenever a backup is created.	
Data and information can be accessed remotely from anywhere.	✔
Improved sustainability, as more documents are stored electronically.	✔
Data is stored more securely.	✔
Cloud accounting software relies on internet access.	

9.8

Once a business has finished with personal data it must store it securely.	
Data should only be used for the explicit purpose for which it was given.	✔
Failure to comply with data protection legislation may result in a fine.	✔
A business must keep personal data that it holds secure from internal and external threats.	✔
Businesses must have appropriate measures and records in place to prove they are complying with data protection principles.	✔
Personal data held by a business must be updated every month.	

9.9

Input controls
Processing controls
Output controls

9.10 **(a)** **Phishing** is a cyberattack that sends a message to a user in an attempt to trick them into opening an email or an attachment that will attack the system.

(b) **Keylogging** is a virus that allows the attacker to record the keystrokes the user makes, and then recreates these strokes to identify passwords, or other sensitive information.

9.11

	Data encryption	Antivirus software
Once installed on a computer system, it runs in the background, providing real-time protection against cyberattacks.		✔
Software that translates data into another form or code that only authorised users, with the necessary password, can read.	✔	

10 Communicating information to stakeholders

10.1

Understandable	
Timely	
Authoritative	
Evaluated	✔
Cost effective	
Efficient	✔

10.2 'The fact that Gita, a qualified accountant who has been the finance manager at the business for three years, produces the report will help to ensure that the information is **authoritative.**'

'Because the report is produced on 4th of each month and the board meeting is a week later, this helps to ensure that the information is **timely**.'

10.3

	True	False
Information provided at the strategic level of an organisation will be detailed rather than summarised.		✔
Information at the management level will be used to translate the strategic goals of an organisation into practical plans.	✔	
Information provided at the strategic level of a business is used to support longer term decisions for the future.	✔	
Information provided at the operational level will be summarised rather than detailed.		✔
Information used at the management level of an organisation will be mostly generated internally.	✔	

10.4

Transactional data is generated from the daily transactions that take place in a business. Typically, this will be from sales and purchases, payments and receipts, and other transactions, and will include huge amounts of data about each individual transaction, ie customers, suppliers, products, prices, locations, and the links between each of these.

10.5

Volume	
Velocity	
Veracity	
Validity	✔

10.6   Any three of the following answers.

Attracting and retaining customers
Focused marketing
To gain competitive advantage
Identify areas of potential risk
Faster innovation
Improve business processes
Fraud detection

10.7   False. An accountant must still apply professional scepticism, even if the big data has been analysed by an external source.

10.8

A flowchart detailing the revised process for staff expenses claims.	Diagram
Monthly profit or loss for the last six months.	Table
The split of the total customers by age.	Pie chart
The seasonal movement in sales over a 12 month period.	Line graph

10.9

	Email	Meeting	Social media	Intranet	Report
Detailed information about the business's results to support an application for a bank loan.					✔
To provide a signed contract to a new supplier.	✔				
To present the features of new products to the staff at a large customer.		✔			
To offer a 25% discount code for anyone ordering by midnight.			✔		

10.10

(a) Three of the following points, or any other sensible suggestion.

- Because the data is presented visually, this will make it easier for non-financial stakeholders to understand.
- Users will have clear overview of the performance of the business.
- Trends and patterns in data will be easier to identify from charts and diagrams.
- Dashboards can be customised to present information that is relevant to the user.
- Data can be accessed in real-time.
- The dashboard can be accessed from any device, in any location, provided there is internet access.

(b) Three of the following points, or any other sensible suggestion.

- Website sales direct to customer make up just over 14% of total sales for the first three months of the year.
- Sales of scarves, hats, gloves, and socks have generally decreased over the three months. This may be due to the weather getting warmer.
- The business has significantly exceeded its sales target for March. This may be due to the end of season sale.
- The business has a significant amount of cash in a deposit account. It may wish to consider investing.
- The sharp fall in sales of scarves in May is probably due to the delayed shipment.

(c)   One of the following points, or any other sensible suggestion.

- There is no information about the profitability of the business. A graph showing the monthly revenue and expenses would help Ashley to understand what profit she is making.
- An analysis of expenses would help Ashley to understand where the business is spending money.

10.11

Misunderstanding	✔
Negative body language	
Information overload	
Lack of planning	✔

Practice assessment 1

Task 1

This task is about organisations and ethics for accountants.

(a)   Identify whether each of the following statements about types of organisations is true or false.

Statement	True	False
The shares of a public limited company are traded on a stock exchange.		
When a partner retires, the partnership must be dissolved immediately.		

(b)   Complete the statements below by selecting the correct option.

In a business with a wide span of control, managers will have......

.... responsibility for a large number of employees.	
.... responsibility for a small number of employees.	
.... responsibility for a wide range of roles.	

Brenborne Ltd is a small website design business, with two directors, Brennan Hughes and Aisha Ashborne, who each own 50% of the shares of the business. Brenborne Ltd employs five website designers and two members of administrative staff.

Brennan and Aisha are considering expanding the business. This will involve investing retained profit, and offering each member of staff up to 2% of the share capital if they wish to invest in the business.

(c)   **(i)**   Identify which of the stakeholders in Brenborne Ltd has the power to decide whether to expand the business or not.

Select **all** that apply.

The bank	
Brennan Hughes	
Aisha Ashborne	
All employees of the business	

(ii) Identify which of these are characteristics of effective governance of a business.

Select **all** options that apply.

Systems that set the goals and objectives of the business.	
Systems that ensure the business maximises the return for the shareholders only.	
Systems that ensure the business is run for the benefit of all stakeholders.	
Legal governance that ensures the business complies with legislation and regulation.	
Directors take responsibility for all decisions, without input from other stakeholder of the business.	

(iii) If some of the employees of Brenborne Ltd decide to invest in the business, identify what effect(s) this will have on Brennan Hughes and Aisha Ashborne.

Select **all** options that apply.

If all members of staff invest in the business, Aisha and Brennan will no longer have overall control of the business.	
Aisha and Brennan's shareholding will be diluted by the share offering.	
All of the new shareholders will be entitled to be directors of the business.	
As shareholders of the business, the employees will have additional rights in relation to the goals and strategy of the business.	
As directors of the business, Brennan and Aisha will have additional responsibilities to the employees now that they are also shareholders.	

Pitkin & Co, a medium sized accounting practice, has several clients that are recruitment businesses. Reggie is the firm's specialist in this type of business. Two of its recruitment clients, Mendel Ltd and Bryce Ltd, are both tendering for the exclusive contract to provide staff to the local authority. Each client has asked Reggie to provide it with advice on its tender document.

(d) **(i)** Identify which two of Reggie's fundamental ethical principles are threatened by the fact that both Mendel Ltd and Bryce Ltd are tendering for the local authority contract.

Professional behaviour	
Confidentiality	
Professional competence and due care	
Objectivity	

Mendel Ltd has realised that Bryce Ltd is also tendering for the local authority contract, so it offers Pitkin & Co an extra £5,000 to act for it exclusively. Bryce Ltd would also like Reggie's exclusive advice and has offered Pitkin & Co an additional £6,000 for this.

(ii) Identify whether the following statements about this situation are true or false.

Statement	True	False
Pitkin & Co is entitled to work for Bryce Ltd simply because it is offering more money for Reggie to carry out the work.		
If Pitkin & Co can put appropriate safeguards in place, Reggie can work on one or other of the clients, but not both.		

(e) Complete the following sentence by selecting the correct options to fill the gaps.

'The AAT Code of Ethics states that accountants should take a _____Gap 1_____ approach to ethics. This requires the accountant _____Gap 2_____ a set of rules exactly as stated.

Gap 1	
rules-based	
principles-based	

Gap 2	
not to simply apply	
to simply apply	

(f) **(i)** Complete the following sentence by selecting the correct option from the list below.

A professional accountant who keeps themself up-to-date with developments in the accounting profession, and takes the appropriate amount of care to ensure that the quality of the work performed meets the high standards expected of the accounting profession, has complied with the fundamental ethical principle of _____.

objectivity	
professional competence and due care	
integrity	

(ii) Identify which one of these would not be considered good continuing professional development (CPD) for an accountant who has been working in practice for several years.

Attending relevant training courses run by AAT.	
Re-reading college notes from when they studied their AAT.	
Watching online webinars provided by HMRC.	

(g) Rayley Ltd is a private limited company with three main shareholders. It has a bank loan for £90,000 which it is paying back over five years, and retained profits of £40,000.

Decide whether the following statements are true or false.

Statement	True	False
The bank is not a stakeholder of Rayley Ltd.		
If the business goes into liquidation, the shareholders will have to pay the balance on the bank loan out of their own personal funds.		

Task 2

This task is about analysing the external environment.

Outside Delights is an established gardening business, operating from several locations across the Midlands. The business provides a variety of gardening services, from weekly visits by gardeners to private gardens, to contracts for maintaining the grounds of local businesses and gardens owned by the local authority. It also offers a redesign and implementation landscaping service.

The owners of Outside Delights have asked Geri, the finance manager, to prepare a report on the business, as they are looking to grow profits and were surprised by some recent figures indicating profits were reducing.

Geri has asked you to help him with the preparation of a PESTLE analysis. He has done some research and has provided the following information to assist you.

Notes from Geri's research:

- Customers are looking to use recycled materials where possible, which are harder to use when landscaping.
- The trend towards less structured, more natural gardens, to encourage wildlife and reduce the use of chemicals, has reduced the number of customers requiring weekly garden maintenance.
- Public funding for open spaces owned by local authorities is being reduced each year.
- The disposable income of individuals has reduced in recent years.
- National minimum wage increases have pushed up the cost of Outside Delight's employees.
- There is low unemployment across the Midlands.
- Several competitors have invested in new websites, incorporating some basic garden design software. Outside Delight's website does not currently include this feature.
- Changes to health and safety legislation have led to new administrative procedures regarding risk assessments for each design job and contract, increasing administrative costs.

(a)   (i)   Identify three of the PESTLE categories.

(ii) For each PESTLE category identified in **(a) (i),** explain how this issue may have an impact on the performance of Outside Delights.

PESTLE Category	Impact on performance

(iii) From the issues identified in **(a) (ii)**, state one action Outside Delights can take as a result of undertaking the PESTLE analysis.

(b) Identify whether each of the following statements about the legal framework for companies and unlimited liability partnerships is true or false.

Statement	True	False
A partnership agreement contains partners' salaries and commission.		
A partnership must have a partnership agreement in place order to operate.		
A limited company is run by the shareholders, on behalf of the directors.		
The directors of a limited company must submit a director's report to shareholders as part of the Annual Accounts submitted to Companies House.		

(c) Complete the following sentences by selecting the correct options:

Shareholders are interested in **maximising/minimising** their investment, linked to dividends and capital growth.

Shareholders are likely to have a **high appetite for risk/reasonable appetite for risk/low appetite for risk.**

Shareholders will normally have **a threshold above/a lower limit below** which they are not prepared to go and risk losing their investment.

(d) Complete the following sentence:

Cloud accounting can be advantageous for a business to use due to **all shareholders/ managers/accounting staff** being able to access and amend real-time financial information.

Task 3

This task is about technology, cyber risk, and data security.

(a) **(i)** Identify which **two** of the following are features of cloud accounting.

Data is hosted on the organisation's own server.	
Improved sustainability, as more documents are stored electronically.	
Data is updated whenever a backup is created.	
Its use relies on the availability of internet access.	
Only one user can access a piece of data at any one time.	

(ii) Identify which **two** of these are disadvantages of cloud accounting.

Data is updated whenever a backup is created.	
Data is backed up automatically to the cloud.	
All stakeholders need to have the cloud accounting software installed on their computers.	
Data and information can be accessed remotely from anywhere.	
Its use relies on the availability of internet access.	

(b) **(i)** Identify which **one** of the following bodies regulates and enforces GDPR in the UK.

National Crime Agency (NCA)	
Her Majesty's Revenue & Customs (HMRC)	
Information Commissioner's Office (ICO)	
Financial Conduct Authority (FCA)	

(ii)   Identify which **two** of the following are valid data protection principles.

All data required must be collected at the same time to avoid multiple requests.
Data can be used for multiple purposes but must not be shared externally with other organisations.
Data must not be held for any longer than necessary, and a business should be able to justify how long it holds data.
Data must be held on a secure external server to prevent misuse.
A business must have appropriate processes in place to prove it complies with data protection principles.

(c)   Decide whether each of the following statements about cyber security is true or false.

Statement	True	False
Data encryption is installed on a computer system to provide real-time protection against cyberattacks.		
A DDoS cyberattack floods an organisation's server with huge numbers of data requests, causing it to freeze up until the attacker's demands are met.		
Browser hijacking changes the user's default home page or search engine allowing the attacker to feed the user with unwanted advertising and popups.		
A firewall will protect the data held by an organisation against internal and external cyberattacks.		

(d)   **(i)**   Identify which **one** of these is not an example of access levels within an accounting system.

Having an in-house IT department with a manager to whom all three IT assistants report.
Passwords that limit access to payroll information to authorised personnel.
Electronic access logs that record which members of staff have entered different parts of the computer system.
Limiting certain users' access to the accounting system to read-only.

(ii) Complete the following sentence by selecting one of the options below.

Integrity controls are built into accounting systems to manage and maintain the _____ of data held by a business.

Options	
presentation and accessibility	
accuracy and completeness	
compliance and consistency	

Linus and Lucy run a small organic vegetable delivery service. They currently work from a converted barn at Lucy's farm where most of the vegetables are grown, and have two delivery vans: one for each of them.

Demand for the service is increasing and they are considering expanding.

(e) **(i)** Identify whether the suggested funding sources for each of the following types of expenditure would be appropriate.

Statement	Funding source	Appropriate	Not appropriate
To pay the wages of two new delivery drivers the business is considering employing.	Bank loan		
To purchase two new delivery vans for the new delivery drivers.	Overdraft		
To purchase larger volumes of packaging material for the additional boxes it plans to deliver.	Working capital		

(ii) Decide whether each of the following statements is true or false.

Statement	Internal stakeholder	External stakeholder
If Linus and Lucy take out a loan with the bank, the bank will become this type of stakeholder.		
The two new delivery drivers that Linus and Lucy plan to employ are this type of stakeholder.		

Task 4

This task is about ethical and legal compliance.

Eli Keszler is a newly qualified accounting technician at Prento & Co, a medium sized firm of accountants with two partners, George Prento and Amelie Desegue. Eli has been on holiday for the last week. He has returned to work to find the following email from Edward Coll, the owner of Ambridge Ltd, which is a client of the firm that operates a delivery company.

From: ecoll@ambridgedelv.com

To: e.keszler@prentoandco.com

Subject: Private & Confidential

Dear Eli

I am very concerned that you appear to be ignoring my emails. I have sent you several now and am considering calling the office to discuss your client care. I wonder what George Prento would say if I told him about our arrangement.

I need to put my bid in for providing the delivery services to Bolt Supplies Ltd by the end of this week. If you don't send me the information you promised about what it currently pays its existing delivery company, then I can't make sure my bid is lower. I know you're concerned about providing me with this information about another of your clients, but this arrangement benefits us all. Bolt Supplies Ltd gets high quality delivery services at a very competitive price, Prento & Co continues to have my business, and you get the £1,000 I offered you for helping me.

Please get back to me as soon as possible.

Regards

Edward

(a)   **(i)**   Explain the two threats Eli is facing to his fundamental ethical principles from the situation detailed in Edward's email.

Eli has discussed the situation with his manager who has hinted he should provide the information to Edward, and they can split the money, and George Prento doesn't need to be involved.

(ii) Briefly explain what action Eli should take in response to the ethical issues arising from this situation.

Prento & Co has recently started an engagement for a new client, Wittenbury Travel Ltd, a large travel agency. As with all its new clients, Prento & Co followed its prescribed customer due diligence procedures prior to taking on Wittenbury Travel Ltd as a client. Libby, a qualified accountant at the firm, has been working at Wittenbury Travel Ltd's premises for the past week and has been concerned about a number of transactions that she has discovered relating to overseas flights. All these sales have been made for cash, and the passengers' names have not been recorded. The total of these sales is over £20,000.

She has asked the managing director of Wittenbury Travel Ltd for more details relating to these transactions, but he has refused to give them to her. She now believes that the client may be involved in money laundering.

(b) **(i)** Explain the actions that Libby must take in respect of her concerns relating to Wittenbury Travel Ltd.

(ii)   Explain whether or not Libby should discuss her concerns with the managing director of Wittenbury Travel Ltd.

(iii)   Explain what consequences Libby may face if she does not take any action in relation to her concerns about the possible money laundering.

Task 5

This task is about the micro-economic environment and sustainability.

Gleewell Ltd is an events management business that organises music and food festivals across the UK. The business has recently undertaken the following initiatives:

- Staff who work at the festivals will be sourced from the local area where each festival is held.

- Festival goers who use transport provided by the business rather than using their own cars will get first choice of the area in which they wish to camp.

- All lights used for the stages will use low energy light bulbs.

(a) **(i)** Identify whether each of the following statements about these initiatives is true or false.

Statement	True	False
Using local staff to work at each festival is an example of social sustainability.		
Using low energy light bulbs is an example economic sustainability.		
Encouraging festival goers not to use their own cars is an example of social sustainability.		
Including details of these initiatives in its CSR report is likely to have a positive impact on the public perception of Gleewell Ltd.		

(ii) Identify which **one** of these is not part of an accountant's responsibility to uphold sustainability.

A public interest duty to protect society as a whole.	
To promote an ethics-based culture within the organisation where they work, and when dealing with clients.	
To ensure the organisation where they work promotes economic sustainability above environmental and social sustainability.	

The following three products are available in the market:

- Fee is a normal good
- Fye is a complementary product for Fee
- Foe is a substitute for Fee

(b)   **(i)**   Identify which **two** of the following will happen if the price of Fee increases.

An increase in demand for Fye	
A decrease in demand for Fee	
An increase in demand for Foe	
No change in demand for Fee	

(ii)   Identify which **one** of the following may cause the demand curve for Fee to shift to the right.

A decrease in the price of a Foe	
An increase in the price of a Foe	
An increase in the cost of Fye	

(c)   Identify whether each of the following statements about competition in the market is true or false.

Statement	True	False
The more that a supplier can differentiate its product, the more competitors it will face in the market.		
A market with one main supplier who controls most, if not all, of the market is known as a monopoly.		

Task 6

This task is about communication and visualisation of data.

Today's date is 8th January 20-5. You work for LifeCycle Luggage Ltd, a business that makes and sells luggage from recycled plastic bottles.

- LifeCycle Luggage Ltd is owned by Tyler Morris and his sister, Nicole, who are also the only directors.

- The luggage is becoming increasingly popular, partly due to some celebrity endorsements in blogs and online in the run up to Christmas, and partly due to its good quality, and range of bright colours.

- The company has recently invested in a new website that launched in November 20-4. Several sales staff were involved in testing it in October 20-4.

- LifeCycle Luggage Ltd employs 62 production staff, five sales and marketing staff, 17 staff in administration, including accounts, and 20 staff in the warehouse.

- The business buys recycled plastic from a supplier in France. Demand for high quality, recycled plastic is growing, so new suppliers are entering the market all the time.

- The company uses several different couriers to deliver web-based orders.

The computerised accounting package has a dashboard of key financial information:

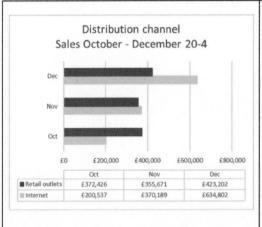

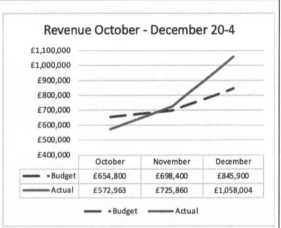

	October	November	December
----- • Budget	£654,800	£698,400	£845,900
———— Actual	£572,963	£725,860	£1,058,004

——— • Budget ———— Actual

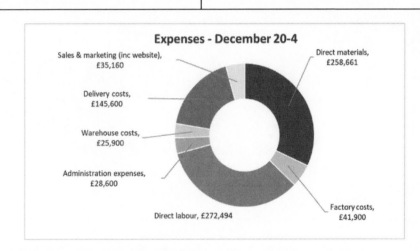

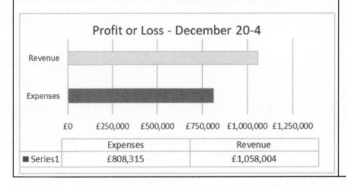

	Expenses	Revenue
■ Series1	£808,315	£1,058,004

Cash balance	
31/12/20-4	£122,500
Change from 30/11/20-4	+ £176,502

(a) **(i)** Discuss the performance of the business over the last three months.

(ii) Identify one positive trend that may be likely to continue in 20-5.

(iii) Suggest one possible action Tyler and Nicole could take to improve profitability further in 20-5.

(b)   Identify which **two** statements are correct.

Sales by product information would identify the least popular lines.	
Sales by product information could be used to determine the most profitable items.	
Sales by product information could be used to set the production plan.	
Sales by product information could be used to update the website.	

(c)   Tyler is considering whether to purchase more machinery to assist in moving products around the factory. Identify the most appropriate method of communicating with the production manager about this matter.

Email	
Telephone call	
Meeting	

Task 7

This task is about risk and big data.

(a)   **(i)**   Identify **one** appropriate risk management strategy to deal with each of the following risks.

	Transfer	Accept	Reduce	Avoid
The risk to a business's employees who work overseas where there has recently been a large earthquake, and more are expected.				
The risk of bad weather causing a tennis final to be postponed.				

(ii)   Identify which of the following is being described here.

'The level of risk an organisation is prepared to accept to achieve its objectives.'

Risk tolerance	
Risk appetite	
Risk threshold	
Risk aversion	

(iii)   Identify the factors that are used to evaluate risk in a risk matrix.

Transferral and Avoidance	
Appetite and Tolerance	
Risk and Reward	
Impact and Likelihood	

(b) Identify which function of an organisation will require each of these pieces of information from the finance function.

Finance function information	Sales & Marketing function	Human Resources function	Information Technology function	Board of directors
Details of overdue customer account balances.				
Potential investment strategies for surplus funds.				
A letter of resignation from a member of the finance staff.				

Waggys & Whiskers is a large pet supplies retailer with outlets across the whole of the UK. The business supplies products for a wide range of pets, and all of its products are also available on its website.

Customers have the option to have home delivery or collection in store.

Customers are offered the opportunity to sign up for the business's loyalty scheme which entitles them to a quarterly set of discounts and the opportunity to earn 'pet points' each time they shop. The business now estimates that 70% of its sales are made to customers with loyalty cards.

If a customer introduces another customer to the scheme, they and the new customer both receive a £10 voucher to spend with Waggys & Whiskers.

(c) **(i)** Identify which characteristic of big data about Waggys & Whiskers is highlighted by each of the following statements.

Statement	Variety	Veracity	Velocity	Value
Waggys & Whiskers collects data about customers with a wide range of pets, who purchase both online and in-store.				
The data processing function that Waggys & Whiskers has is constantly processing thousands of orders each day across its stores and website.				
Waggys & Whiskers analyses the data it collects to identify trends and anomalies in the purchasing patterns of its customers.				
The analysis Waggys & Whiskers has carried out on its customer data has allowed it to target customers with relevant and attractive discount vouchers.				

The sales director at Waggys & Whiskers has asked for a detailed breakdown of sales of dog food by product, month and between stores and online. The finance assistant has used tables, graphs, and colour coding to simplify the information.

(ii)   Complete the following statement by selecting one of the options below.

The way in which the finance assistant has presented the data helps to ensure that the information is ....

...... authoritative.	
...... cost effective.	
...... complete.	
...... understandable.	

Practice assessment 2

Task 1

This task is about organisations and ethics for accountants.

(a) Identify whether each of the following statements about types of organisations is true or false.

Statement	True	False
The main rules that govern charities are included in the Companies Act.		
Services in the public sector are examples of not-for-profit organisations.		

(b) Identify the contribution to the business, and the requirements from the business, for the stakeholders in the table below.

Stakeholder	Contribution to the business	Requirements from the business
Shareholders	Gap1	Gap 2
Finance providers	Gap 3	Gap 4

Gap 1	
Compliance with ethical codes	
Capital investment	
Training and development	

Gap 2	
Profitability	
Training and development	
Knowledge and skills	

Gap 3	
Substantiality	
Loaned funds	
Capital investment	

Gap 4	
Loyalty	
Regular repayments	
Profitability	

(c) Identify which type of organisational structure has each of the following characteristics.

Characteristic	Flat organisational structure	Tall organisational structure	Centralised control	Decentralised control
Authority for decision-making is given to lower levels of management, leading to a more collaborative working environment.				
Decisions are imposed on staff rather than allowing the staff to contribute to the decision-making process.				
Information in this type of organisation can pass up and down the chain of command quickly.				

Geraint is a student member of AAT who works in the finance department at Gravely Ltd, a manufacturing business. Geraint has posted an offensive comment in reply to a post by a customer on Gravely Ltd's social media page. A number of customers have complained to the business about the fact that the post was in bad taste.

(d) **(i)** Identify which **one** of his fundamental ethical principles Geraint has breached by posting the comment.

Professional competence and due care	
Objectivity	
Confidentiality	
Professional behaviour	

(ii) Identify whether each of the following organisations can bring disciplinary procedures against Geraint in this situation.

Organisation	Can bring disciplinary procedures	Cannot bring disciplinary procedures
AAT		
Gravely Ltd		
HMRC		

(e) For each of the following situations, decide what type of threat it creates to the accountant's fundamental ethical principles.

Situation	Familiarity threat	Intimidation threat	Advocacy threat	Self-review threat
A client tells its accountant that it may consider changing its accountant if its fees are not reduced by 10%.				
A client has asked its accountant to write an introduction in its brochure for a new share issue, stating what an excellent investment it would be.				
A finance director of a manufacturing business plays golf every weekend with the managing director of one of its main suppliers.				

(f) Identify what the following sentence describes.

'An attitude that includes a questioning mind, being alert to conditions which may indicate possible misstatement due to error or fraud, and a critical assessment of evidence'.

Professional competence and due care	
Professional scepticism	
Integrity	
Professional behaviour	

Betty has been operating as a sole trader from a number of years. Sales have grown over this time, and she now has three people working for her. Betty is considering becoming a limited company.

(g) **(i)** Identify which **two** of these are disadvantages of an organisation being incorporated.

The higher costs associated with record keeping and submitting annual returns.	
Access to finance, such as bank loans, may be easier than for a sole trader.	
Shareholders' liability for the debts of the business are limited to the amount they have invested in the business.	
Information that is filed at Companies House about the business and its finances can be accessed by anyone.	

(ii) Identify which of the following are internal stakeholders of a business. Choose **one** option.

Customers	
Suppliers	
Directors	
Banks	

Task 2

This task is about analysing the external environment.

Forestware makes high quality fine china plates, cups, and saucers. Approximately 30% of sales are made in the UK, but 70% are exported to the Far East and the USA. Customers are invoiced by Forestware in local currency. Export tariffs apply for both these locations. Raw materials are purchased from across Europe, as well as the UK. Some import tariffs apply.

The business has one factory currently operating in the UK. The production process is highly labour intensive, and all the workers are highly skilled. The company has faced some difficulties recruiting appropriately skilled labour, due to a lack of government investment in education and training in the area in recent years. Some local competitors are currently setting up apprenticeship programmes, to access new government funding.

Some product ranges are popular with long-standing customers, who continue to purchase new and replacement items. Despite constant changes in trends for homeware, Forestware has not updated its range of designs for some time. Customers have also moved away from keeping one set of china for 'best' and, increasingly, are having only one set of tableware that is used every day.

(a) Using the table below, for each of the three specified PESTLE categories:

    (i) Identify one threat facing Forestware.

    (ii) Explain one action Forestware could take to reduce the threat under each category.

Category	(i) Threat	(ii) Action to reduce the threat
Political		
Economic		
Social		

(iii) Identify one of the remaining PESTLE categories.

(b) Match each of these technologies to one advantage it brings to accounting systems used in business.

Statement	Advantage
Automation	
Machine learning	
Qualified electronic signature	
Blockchain	

Options
Complex data can be analysed
Encryption of data, so only authorised users can access it
Improved data integrity
Quick and efficient validation of parties involved

(c) Identify whether each of the following statements about unlimited liability partnerships is true or false.

Statement	True	False
A partnership must cease to operate when a partner retires.		
Goodwill in a partnership is defined as the difference between the value of a business as a whole and the net value of its assets.		

(d) Complete the following sentences about financial statements of limited companies.

Financial statements of limited companies **must/must not** be prepared under International Accounting Standards. Directors of large, limited companies **must/must not** ensure the financial statements are audited.

Task 3

This task is about technology, cyber risk, and data security.

(a)   Identify whether each of the following statements about data protection is true or false.

Statement	True	False
A business owner who breaches data protection legislation may face a prison sentence.		
A data subject can request for data a business holds about them to be destroyed at any point.		
Once a business has used personal data for the purpose it was collected, it should delete it immediately.		
In the UK the Information Commissioner's Office is the body that regulates and enforces GDPR.		

(b)   Identify which **two** of these are features of cloud accounting.

The accounting system is automatically updated each time a piece of data is added.	
The accounting system is held on the organisation's server and backed up to the cloud at predefined intervals.	
The accounting system will incorporate an element of Artificial Intelligence (AI), which means that staff will not need to be trained in how to use it.	
Cloud accounting will increase the IT costs of the business and reduce the software costs.	
Access to cloud accounting relies on users having internet access and appropriate software installed on their computers.	

(c)   (i)   Identify which of the characteristics of a service business is being described by each of the statements below.

Statement	Inseparability	Perishability	Intangibility	Variability
The service has to be used as it is provided as any unused service cannot be stored for future use.				
The service will be specifically designed to meet the needs of the individual customer or client.				
The provision and consumption of the service happen at the same time.				
The service is not generally a physical product.				

Sasha runs a business that provides cleaning services to local businesses. She has two supervisors, one of whom supervises a team of office cleaners, and the other a team of domestic cleaners. The two supervisors report directly to Sasha.

(ii)   Complete the following statement by selecting **one** of the options below.

This demonstrates that Sasha's business benefits from _____ .

Options	
a tall organisational structure	
staff autonomy	
defined responsibilities for staff members	

(d)   Match each of the following statements to what is being described, using each option once.

Part of a computer application designed to manage and maintain the completeness and accuracy of data.	Anti-virus software
A barrier that sits between a business's internal computer network and the public internet.	Integrity controls
Software that runs in the background and provides real-time protection to a business's computer system again cyberattacks.	Firewall

(e) Identify what type of cyberattack is being described by each of the following statements.

	Spyware	DDoS	Ransomware	Malware
The general term for malicious software, often inserted into computer via phishing emails, that can introduce viruses, keyloggers, spyware, worms, or ransomware.				
This allows the attacker to watch the operations of the business without being seen by the user.				
A cyberattack that locks the user out of their information system and makes demands, usually money, to prevent further disruption.				

Task 4

This task is about ethical and legal compliance.

Riley is a part-qualified accountant who works for Brightings Ltd, a business that produces industrial lighting. He has been asked by the finance director to prepare the year-end information for the external auditors relating to non-current assets. The finance director is unable to do this work as she is renegotiating a loan with the bank. Previously Riley has only ever carried out depreciation calculations as part of his AAT studies, and the schedules that are required for Brightings Ltd are much more complicated.

The finance director has mentioned that Riley's pay review is due next month and, as part of this review, she will take into account how well he carries out this work.

(a) **(i)** Explain which **two** of Riley's fundamental ethical principles are being most threatened in this situation.

(ii) Explain **two** safeguards that could be put in place to address this threat.

Jorja, another accountant who works at Brightings Ltd, has been asked to prepare a short presentation for the finance department about money laundering as she has recently completed some relevant CPD on this subject. The business has recently had to terminate the employment of one of its sales team as they had been found to be involved in the money laundering offence of 'integration'. Consequently, it is keen to make sure everyone knows what is expected of them.

(b)   **(i)**   Provide a brief explanation of what money laundering is.

```


```

(ii)   List the three stages of the money laundering process in the order in which they occur.

```


```

(iii)   Explain the term 'integration' in relation to money laundering.

```


```

Task 5

This task is about the micro-economic environment and sustainability.

Cyrus & Co is a medium sized firm of accountants. The managing director of one of its newest clients, Rosslyn Organics Ltd, has recently contacted Cyrus & Co to discuss the firm's attitude to sustainability and sustainable development. She has explained to him that as part of Rosslyn Organics Ltd's CSR, it only trades with businesses that can prove they are keen to promote sustainability and sustainable development. She has asked for evidence from Cyril & Co that it focuses on its 'triple bottom line when measuring its performance'.

(a) **(i)** In relation to sustainability, identify which of the following is abbreviated to CSR.

Corporate sustainability reporting	
Critical social responsibility	
Corporate social responsibility	
Corporate sustainable responsibility	

As part of the evidence of its focus on sustainability, Cyrus & Co has listed the three points in the table below.

(ii) For each point, identify which of the three elements of sustainability it supports.

Evidence	Economic responsibility	Social responsibility	Environmental responsibility
Where possible, Cyrus & Co sources goods and services from local suppliers.			
The standard business email signature for all staff at Cyrus & Co includes the words: 'Think before you print! Do you need to print this email?'			
Cyrus & Co encourages its staff to take part in local charitable activities and provides them with time off work, or financial support, to do so.			

(iii) Identify whether the following statement is true or false.

Statement	True	False
Accountants in practice must ensure that the firm they work for upholds sustainability and sustainable development, but this duty does not extend to ensuring their clients do the same.		

(b) **(i)** Identify which **one** of the following events may cause a shift in the supply curve for a normal good.

Increase in the cost of production labour	
Increase in the price of the normal good	
Decrease in the VAT charged on the sale of the normal good	
Decrease in the price of the normal good	

(ii) Identify whether each of the following statements is true or false.

Statement	True	False
Substitute products are those which consumers will buy regardless of whether their income changes.		
Normal goods are those for which demand increases when income increases, and goes down if income decreases.		
Cheaper goods for which demand generally decreases as income rises are known as necessity goods.		
If the price of a normal good decreases, demand for a complementary good will generally increase.		

Task 6

This task is about communication and visualisation of data.

Today's date is 8th July 20-8. You work for Villas Coaches Ltd, a coach and minibus hire business.

The company owns 20 49-seater coaches, 10 of which run on petrol, with the remainder running on electricity. It has recently invested in eight new 16-seater hybrid minibuses, that run on either petrol or electricity.

The company has several contracts with schools and other companies to provide buses for student transportation Monday to Friday during term time. The 49-seater coaches are usually used for these contracts. Schools were on holiday for two days in January 20-8, and one week in February 20-8. Competition is fierce for these school contracts, as there are several coach operators in the area, so margins are low. Tenders have been made for the next academic year, and contracts are due to be awarded at the end of July 20-8.

The company offers 30 days credit to all contract customers. Ad hoc hirers, who often hire the 16-seater vehicles, pay a deposit when the booking is made, and pay the balance at the end of the booking period.

The finance manager is off sick, and the managing director has asked you to explain why the accounting software uses a dashboard (shown on the next page), rather than more traditional ways of presenting financial information. She would also like some explanation of the data on the dashboard.

The accounting software includes a dashboard, shown below:

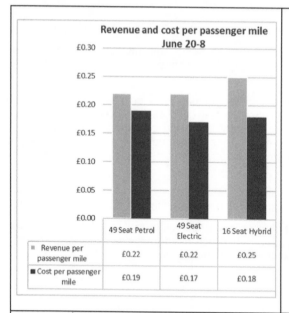

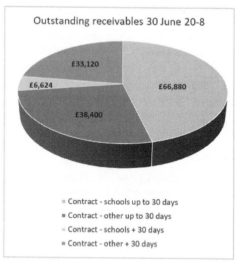

Revenue and cost per passenger mile June 20-8	49 Seat Petrol	49 Seat Electric	16 Seat Hybrid
Revenue per passenger mile	£0.22	£0.22	£0.25
Cost per passenger mile	£0.19	£0.17	£0.18

Outstanding receivables 30 June 20-8
- Contract - schools up to 30 days
- Contract - other up to 30 days
- Contract - schools + 30 days
- Contract - other + 30 days

£33,120 £6,624 £66,880 £38,400

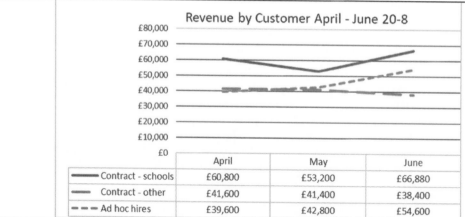

Revenue by Customer April - June 20-8	April	May	June
Contract - schools	£60,800	£53,200	£66,880
Contract - other	£41,600	£41,400	£38,400
Ad hoc hires	£39,600	£42,800	£54,600

Driver costs as a percentage of revenue	April	May	June
Contract - schools	50%	63%	64%
Contract - other	50%	63%	64%
Ad hoc hires	50%	50%	50%

(a)   **(i)**   Briefly explain why the dashboard uses charts and graphs, rather than the layout of financial statements.

(ii)   Explain **three** areas of concern for Villas Coaches Ltd in the performance for the three months to June 20-8.

(iii) Explain one possible improvement to profitability that could be made, that is highlighted by the dashboard.

(iv) Suggest **one** further piece of information which could be useful to include on the dashboard.

The business has decided to replace all petrol vehicles with either electric or hybrid ones.

(b) Identify **two** pieces of information the business should provide to the bank to obtain a loan for this expenditure.

The most recent set of financial statements	
Access to the accounting software, including the dashboard	
Copies of all drivers' employment contracts	
Business forecasts, incorporating the new vehicles	

The business wants to inform its stakeholders of its move to using more sustainable vehicles.

(c) Identify which method of communicating this decision to its passengers would not be appropriate. Select **one** option.

Email	
Social media posts	
Posters on coaches	

Task 7

This task is about risk and big data.

(a)　(i)　Identify which **two** of these are qualities of big data.

Velocity	
Variability	
Volume	
Valid	

　(ii)　Identify the source of the big data described in each of the following statements.

Statement	Social data	Machine data	Transactional data
Data from satellite tracking that shows the routes and timings of deliveries made by a courier.			
The number, and timing, of views of an organisation's promotional video on YouTube.			
Data about products, prices, and the timing of customer purchases, recorded at a supermarket checkout.			

(b)　(i)　Identify whether each of the following statements about risk is true or false.

Statement	True	False
A business that pays for insurance on the inventory held in its warehouse against fire is an example of risk avoidance.		
Risk averse stakeholders will be willing to accept a lower return in order to minimise the risk they face.		
The risk to a business of failing to maintain health and safety standards in its factories overseas is an example of reputational risk.		
A new supplier entering the market for a product at a lower price is an example of a strategic risk.		

(ii) Identify which **one** of the following would not normally be classified as an operational risk.

The risk of over-reliance on a key member of production staff.	
The risk of fraudulent transactions going undetected in the payroll system.	
A shortage of labour to work in the production department of a business.	
The risk that defective products go unnoticed by the quality assurance department.	

(c) Freida is the finance manager at Cromwells Ltd. Every month, the business pays overtime to its production staff based on the business's clocking in and out system. Each day employees scan their staff card when they start, and again when they leave.

Freida downloads the hours worked from the clocking in and out system and the accounting system automatically applies the basic and overtime rates.

Freida prepares a weekly report that shows a bar chart of budgeted overtime compared with actual overtime, which is sent to the production manager to review and approve.

Complete the following sentences by selecting the correct words from the picklist.

The fact that Freida extracts the information about overtime hours worked from the clocking in and out system will help to ensure that the information is	Picklist 1
Presenting the information to the production manager as a graph helps to ensure that the information is	Picklist 2

Picklist 1	
cost effective.	
understandable.	
accurate.	

Picklist 2	
timely.	
understandable.	
authoritative.	

Practice
assessment 3

Task 1

This task is about organisations and ethics for accountants.

(a) Identify whether each of the following statements about types of organisations is true or false.

Statement	True	False
A sole trader must make an annual return to Companies House.		
If a partnership is formed without a partnership agreement, the partnership will be governed by the Partnership Act.		

Sasha's Sweet Delights is a successful cake making business which is owned and run by Sasha Briars. The business employs four bakers, three cake decorators and two part-time administrative staff. The business is visited at appropriate times by a food safety officer from the local authority.

Sasha has secured additional funding which can be invested in two different options:

1) New premises with new, state-of-the-art, cake decorating equipment.

2) Paying off the balance on the business loan from the bank that Sasha took out when she set up the business.

(b) **(i)** Identify which **one** of the stakeholders in Sasha's Sweet Delights has the power to decide which option to choose.

Administrative staff	
Bakers	
Sasha Briars	
Local authority	

(ii) Apart from Sasha, identify which **one** of the stakeholders has the greatest interest in the investment decision.

Administrative staff	
Bakers	
Cake decorators	
Local authority	

(iii) Identify who is responsible for the corporate governance at Sasha's Sweet Delights.

Select **one** option.

The bank	
Sasha Briars	
Local authority	
The Government	

(c) Identify which **three** of these are common features of business organisations.

Co-operation	
Defined structure	
Profitability targets	
Goal congruence	
Limited liability	

Confidentiality is one of the five fundamental ethical principles that a professional accountant is expected to adhere to.

(d) **(i)** Decide whether the following statement about confidentiality is true or false.

Statement	True	False
In addition to being a fundamental ethical principle, confidentiality is also a legal obligation.		

(ii)   Identify whether an accountant can, or cannot, disclose confidential information in each of the following situations.

Situation	Can be disclosed	Cannot be disclosed
A request from a local builder's merchants for financial information about a client who has asked to buy from them on credit terms.		
Information about a client for whom the accountant ceased working three years ago.		
The accountant has been asked to provide documents about a client as part of an ongoing court case.		
AAT is conducting a disciplinary inquiry into one of the partners in the accounting practice for which the accountant works.		

Deidra Bassano works as an accountant in a medium sized firm of accountants. One of her clients, Jon Joffrey, has recently used the business to help prepare a loan application to invest in expanding his business. Unfortunately, the bank was only prepared to lend part of the money he required. Jon has found another potential investor and has asked Deidra to speak to them and explain what an excellent investment opportunity it would be for them.

(e)   Complete the following statement by selecting the correct options to complete the gaps.

Jon Joffrey's request is ___Gap 1_____ to Deidra's fundamental ethical principle of _____Gap 2_____ .

Gap 1	
a familiarity threat	
an advocacy threat	

Gap 2	
confidentiality	
objectivity	

(f)   Identify which **one** of the following is not a key organisational value for ensuring compliance with regulations and ethical principles.

Providing fair treatment, decent wages, and good working conditions for all employees	
Appropriate use of social media	
Paying suppliers a fair price and on time	
Ensuring an annual dividend is paid to shareholders	

(g) Identify whether each of the following statements about organisational structure is true or false.

Statement	True	False
Decentralised control leads to a more collaborative working environment.		
An organisation with a number of new products being developed will benefit from a matrix structure.		
A manager in a smaller organisation is likely to have a narrower span of control.		
A business with separate departments for finance, sales, production, distribution, and human resources, is likely to have a functional structure.		

Task 2

This task is about analysing the external environment.

Molly's Milkshakes was set up three years ago by Molly Middleton, a dairy farmer in Yorkshire.

It produces different flavours of organic milkshake, selling them to local retailers, cafés, restaurant owners, and a small local supermarket chain. The business has grown and now uses milk from several farmers across the county, which it transports to the production and bottling plant. Some of the milk is supplied by farms located over 50 miles away.

All the bottles Molly's Milkshakes uses are recyclable. Other drinks manufacturers are now using bottles made from recycled plastic, or finding alternative, bio-degradable packaging. Whilst some competitors have launched milkshake ranges using oat or soya milk, Molly's Milkshakes does not currently offer an alternative, non-dairy product. Molly Middleton grows organic oats on her farm, some of which are used as cattle feed.

The recipes used in the milkshakes the business produces currently contain some sugar. Consumers are becoming increasingly aware of the need to make healthier choices when purchasing drinks. Government policy is also promoting reduced sugar in milk drinks, by taxing the sugar content. New legislation is also being introduced that requires more detailed analysis of the ingredients and nutritional values on the label of these drinks.

(a) Using the table on the next page, for each of the three specified PESTLE categories:

(i) Identify **one** threat facing Molly's Milkshakes.

(ii) Explain **one** action Molly's Milkshakes could take to reduce the threat under each category.

Category	(i) Threat	(ii) Action to reduce the threat
Social		
Legal		
Environmental		

(iii)   Identify **one** of the remaining PESTLE categories.

(b)   Complete each of the following statements about unlimited liability partnerships by selecting the correct words.

When a partner joins a partnership, **all/some/one** of the partners must agree to the change.

Goodwill must be determined when a **partner retires from/partner joins/partner retires from, or joins,** the partnership.

(c)   Identify whether each of the following statements is true or false about limited companies.

Statement	True	False
All limited companies are required to have an Articles of Association.		
All financial statements of limited companies must include notes to the accounts.		

(d)   Identify **two** benefits of blockchain to the role of the accountant.

Protection against hacking	
Forecasting future data accurately	
Reducing costs and improving efficiency of record keeping	
Lower IT costs	

Task 3

This task is about technology, cyber risk, and data security.

(a)   For each of the following categories of technology, identify one advantage it contributes to a business's success.

Advantage	Artificial Intelligence (AI)	Electronic document filing	Block-chain	Data analytics
Provides certainty about the integrity of data by protecting against unauthorised access.				
Identifies anomalies in data and diagnoses why they may have occurred.				
Complex data can be analysed to form the basis of future decision-making.				
Protects documents and business records against fire or flood.				

(b)   (i)   Identify the type of cyberattack that is occurring in each of the following situations.

Situation	Keylogging	Phishing
Ramona has received an email telling her to click on the link to pay an overdue invoice.		
The anti-virus software at Rolo Ltd has picked up an instance of malware that is recording what Ramona is typing into her computer.		

(ii)   Identify which **two** of the following are risks to a business created by cyberattacks.

Corruption or misuse of customer information by a third party	
Increased inventory insurance costs	
Operational risk of the loss of key staff	
Temporary or permanent IT system failure	

(c)   (i)   Complete the following statement by selecting **one** of the options below.

Once a business has finished using personal data it should ....

Options	
.... ask the data subject what they want it to do with the data.	
.... hold on to the data in case it is needed in the future.	
.... destroy the data in a secure manner.	

(ii) Decide whether each of the following statements about data protection is true or false.

	True	False
There is no maximum limit on the fine that can be imposed for breaches of data protection principles.		
Data should be used only for the explicit purpose for which it was given.		
It is up to the data subject to ensure that the data an organisation holds about them is accurate and up-to-date.		

Ffion runs a small marketing business based in Dorset in the UK. Her business works with other local businesses to market and promote their goods and services. She employs two members of staff who specialise in marketing, and one part-time administrator. Ffion has always maintained her accounting records using spreadsheets. A bookkeeper comes in on a quarterly basis to prepare and submit the VAT Return, and, at the end of the year, to prepare the annual accounts.

The bookkeeper has suggested that Ffion might consider buying an off-the-shelf cloud accounting package.

(d) **(i)** Identify which **three** of these would be advantages of Ffion moving to a cloud accounting system.

Ffion would be able to extend her business to offer services internationally.	
The cloud accounting system could link to the business's bank account and post some of the transactions automatically.	
Ffion would no longer need to maintain her spreadsheet accounting system.	
Ffion would no longer need to employ the bookkeeper as the system will prepare the VAT Returns and annual accounts automatically.	
Ffion will need to have the same cloud accounting software as the bookkeeper uses.	
The bookkeeper would be able to access the accounting system in real-time.	

(ii) Identify whether each of the following statements about the way Ffion's business is operated is true or false.

	True	False
Ffion is the only stakeholder in the business.		
Because the business offers a service to its customers, it is easier to have a standard price list.		
The majority of Ffion's expenses will be staff costs.		

Task 4

This task is about ethical and legal compliance.

Charlie is a qualified AAT member who works as a sole practitioner. For several years he has provided accounting services to Finleys Ltd, a family firm that makes kitchen equipment. Finleys Ltd has recently secured several large orders from two national retail chains, and is looking for someone to invest additional capital in the business. Charlie's wife, Suranne, has recently inherited some money and wants to invest it in a suitable business.

(a) Explain why it is not acceptable for Suranne to invest in Finleys Ltd. Your explanation should include:

- Which one of Charlie's fundamental principles would be threatened if Suranne does invest
- The type of threat this represents
- A safeguard Charlie could put in place to address this threat if Surannne does invest

Keisha, a professional accountant, has taken a year out to go travelling around the world. She is due to return to the small accounting practice she works for.

(b) Briefly explain which of Keisha's fundamental ethical principles is most threatened by the fact that she has spent a year away from work. Include one thing she can do to address this.

George is one of the part-qualified accountants who works in the finance department of Inkwell Limited, a family owned company, which makes and sells ink for the printing industry. George reports to the financial controller.

George has noticed that a customer, Kazamm Ltd, regularly pays for the ink it orders in cash, and has calculated that over the last 18 months these cash sales have totalled more than £170,000. No one is able to tell him why the business always pays in cash and George is beginning to suspect that money laundering is taking place.

George is aware that the managing director of Inkwell Ltd is a shareholder of Kazamm Ltd.

(c) **(i)** Explain what issues arise from this situation for Inkwell Ltd, and what action George needs to take with respect to Kazamm Ltd, including informing third parties.

Task 5

This task is about the micro-economic environment and sustainability.

(a) **(i)** For each point, identify which of the three elements of sustainability the organisational policy supports.

Organisational policy	Economic/ Financial responsibility	Social responsibility	Environmental responsibility
Bamberoli Ltd has a policy to match any charitable fundraising carried out by members of staff, up to a maximum of £500 per staff member per year.			
Pandaworks Ltd manufactures toilet tissue. It has undertaken to plant a tree for every pack of its product that is sold.			
Greener Groundwork Ltd is an environmentally friendly landscape gardening business. All projects it tenders for are costed in detail and include a built-in 25% profit margin.			

(ii) Complete the following sentences about sustainability by selecting the correct option from the picklists.

Sustainable development meets the needs of the present without	Picklist 1
Professional accountants should	Picklist 2

Picklist 1		Picklist 2	
compromising the profitability of the business.		require all clients to produce a corporate social responsibility report.	
compromising the ability of future generations to meet their own needs.		report clients without appropriate sustainability targets, immediately.	
damaging the environment in any way.		promote sustainable practices in their workplace.	

(b) **(i)** Identify which **one** of the following describes the equilibrium price of a normal good.

The point where the price and the cost of a normal good are equal.	
All competitors in the market sell a product for the same price.	
The price at which supply and demand are equal.	
There is a monopoly in the market, so the price remains unchanged to all customers.	

(ii) Identify whether each of the following statements about the micro-economic environment are true or false.

Statement	True	False
A change in price of a good or service will result in a shift along the demand curve.		
The price mechanism only works to find the equilibrium price for necessity goods.		
A decrease in the number of buyers in the market for a product will make the market more competitive.		
Set up costs are likely to be more of a barrier to entry for Paulette who is setting up as a bookkeeper than for Lionel who is setting up a café and cake-making business.		

Task 6

This task is about communication and visualisation of data.

Today's date is 12th January 20-3. You work for Bradleys, a second-hand car dealership. It has five sales locations across the country.

Tonya Bradley, the owner, has been trading for several years. The business started in Bristol and has expanded, opening a new branch every year.

Each branch is managed by a sales manager. Sales staff are paid bonuses based on the number of cars sold and the profits earned. Sales staff in both the Worcester and Stratford-Upon-Avon branches have left since July 20-2, and the sales managers have found it difficult to replace them. This may be due to a lot of local competition, combined with the fact that the basic salary offered is low, even though the sales bonuses are generous. New staff have been secured and are due to start in January 20-3.

Tonya Bradley oversees the Bristol branch. She was on extended sick leave in September and October and returned to work, part-time, in November. While she was away, the sales manager amended the pricing on medium-sized family cars and small hatchbacks.

The financial controller, who usually goes through the dashboard from the accounting software with Tonya, is off sick, so Tonya has asked you to help her to interpret the information.

The dashboard showing recent performance is shown below:

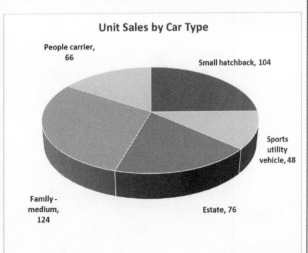

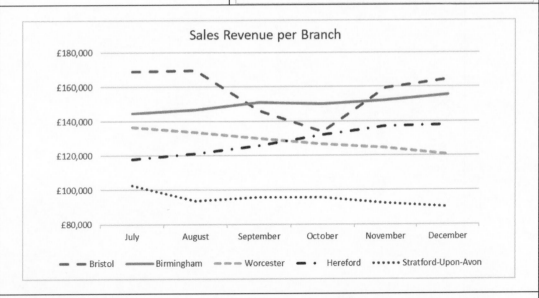

Product type	July	August	September	October	November	December
Small hatchback	18	18	17	14	17	20
Sports utility vehicle	8	8	8	8	8	8
Estate	13	13	12	12	13	13
Family - medium	24	24	15	14	24	23
People carrier	11	11	11	11	11	11
Total	**74**	**74**	**63**	**59**	**73**	**75**

(a) **(i)** Discuss the performance of the business over the six months to 31 December 20-2 and the expected performance for January 20-3.

(ii) Suggest one further piece of information which could be useful to include on the dashboard.

Tonya has been reviewing the way she communicates with the branches, as she has no formal communication policy. She has asked your opinion on the best way to communicate with the sales managers on two matters.

(b) Identify which of these is the best communication method for each of the following matters.

Matter	Email	Meeting	Telephone
Tonya wants to amend the basic salary and bonus scheme, to make it more appealing to the salespeople. The views of some of the current sales team would be useful.			
Tonya would like to open a new branch in Leicester and wants to inform current staff members of the job description, as they may wish to apply for the sales manager role.			

Task 7

This task is about risk and big data.

(a) **(i)** Identify which function of an organisation will provide each of these pieces of information to the finance function.

Finance function requirement	Production function	Human Resources function	Information Technology function	Distribution function
Costs and schedule for servicing delivery vehicles.				
Number of units manufactured by staff on piecework pay.				
Salaries for new employees.				

(ii) Milos works in the finance department at Betterfold Ltd. It is 4pm on Wednesday afternoon, and the finance director has asked Milos to run a detailed report for the board of directors meeting the next day at 9am. He wants it to show the sales of each product for each month of the year compared with the budget. Milos is worried that he may have to rush to complete the work in time.

Milos suggests that, as several of the board of directors do not have a financial background, it might be a good idea to present some of the information using graphs and/or diagrams. The finance director is not keen on this idea and tells Milos he wants it to be produced in a spreadsheet and he can 'talk them through it.'

Complete the following sentences by selecting the correct words from the picklist.

Milos's suggestion to present the information using graphs and charts would help to ensure that the information is ….	Picklist 1
The fact that Milos may have to rush to complete the work on time means that the information may not be ….	Picklist 2

Picklist 1	
relevant	
accurate	
understandable	

Picklist 2	
timely	
accurate	
relevant	

(b) **(i)** Identify which of the following is being described here.

'The amount of money an organisation is prepared to risk losing if a project fails.'

Risk tolerance	
Risk appetite	
Risk threshold	
Risk aversion	

(ii) Identify the appropriate risk management strategy that is being used to deal with each of the following risks.

	Transfer	Accept	Reduce	Avoid
A chemical business that subcontracts the disposal of hazardous waste to an expert waste management company.				
A website business that carries out regular staff training on the data protection principles included in GDPR.				

Brilliant Burgers is a multinational chain of fast food restaurants, where customers have the option to eat in, takeaway, or order for delivery by third party delivery companies.

The business collects large amounts of data from the electronic till points in all its restaurants and on its website, including items ordered, time of day orders are placed, and combinations of food and drinks. Many of its customers sign up for the Brilliant Burgers Bonuses. This loyalty scheme gives them money-off vouchers, and loyalty points for every purchase they make which they can exchange for free food or drinks. In return, the business gets further information about the individual customers, including age, location, gender, family demographic and spending.

The business also uses data collected by the delivery companies it uses which allows it to analyse the location of its customers across the world.

(c)   Identify whether each of the following statements about the data it collects is true or false.

Statement	True	False
One of the advantages to Brilliant Burgers of collecting large amounts of data about its customers is that it can establish trends in purchasing and patterns of behaviour.		
Because customers have chosen to sign up for the loyalty scheme, Brilliant Burgers can share the customer data with the delivery companies that it uses.		
The data that Brilliant Burgers is collecting will allow it to analyse its market share.		
Proper analysis of the data collected by Brilliant Burgers will help the business to decide where to open further branches.		

Answers to practice assessment 1

Task 1

(a)

Statement	True	False
The shares of a public limited company are traded on a stock exchange.	✔	
When a partner retires, the partnership must be dissolved immediately.		✔

(b) In a business with a wide span of control, managers will have responsibility for a large number of employees.

(c) **(i)**

The bank	
Brennan Hughes	✔
Aisha Ashborne	✔
All employees of the business	

(ii)

Systems that set the goals and objectives of the business.	✔
Systems that ensure the business maximises the return for the shareholders only.	
Systems that ensure the business is run for the benefit of all stakeholders.	✔
Legal governance that ensures the business complies with legislation and regulation.	✔
Directors take responsibility for all decisions, without input from other stakeholder of the business.	

(iii)

If all members of staff invest in the business, Aisha and Brennan will no longer have overall control of the business.	
Aisha and Brennan's shareholding will be diluted by the share offering.	✔
All of the new shareholders will be entitled to be directors of the business.	
As shareholders of the business, the employees will have additional rights in relation to the goals and strategy of the business.	✔
As directors of the business, Brennan and Aisha will have additional responsibilities to the employees now that they are also shareholders.	✔

(d)   **(i)**

Professional behaviour	
Confidentiality	✔
Professional competence and due care	
Objectivity	✔

(ii)

Statement	True	False
Pitkin & Co is entitled to work for Bryce Ltd simply because it is offering more money for Reggie to carry out the work.		✔
If Pitkin & Co can put appropriate safeguards in place, Reggie can work on one or other of the clients, but not both.	✔	

(e)   The AAT Code of Ethics states that accountants should take a **principles-based** approach to ethics. This requires the accountant **not to simply apply** a set of rules exactly as stated.

(f)   **(i)**   A professional accountant who keeps themself up-to-date with developments in the accounting profession, and takes the appropriate amount of care to ensure that the quality of the work performed meets the high standards expected of the accounting profession, has complied with the fundamental ethical principle of **professional competence and due care**.

(ii)

Attending relevant training courses run by AAT.	
Re-reading college notes from when they studied their AAT.	✔
Watching online webinars provided by HMRC.	

(g)

Statement	True	False
The bank is not a stakeholder of Rayley Ltd.		✔
If the business goes into liquidation, the shareholders will have to pay the balance on the bank loan out of their own personal funds.		✔

Task 2

(a) (i) Any three of:

Political
Environmental
Social
Technological
Legal
Economic

(ii) Answer should include three of the following, depending on the categories included in the answer to **(a) (i)**.

Category	Impact on performance
Political	Public funding is being reduced for maintaining public gardens, including those that Outside Delights currently has contracts for. This means that the value of these contracts to Outside Delights is reducing, which will adversely affect the profitability of Outside Delights.
Economic	Disposable income of individuals, ie private customers, has reduced recently, so less money is available to spend on 'luxuries' such as a having a gardener or relandscaping.

Changes in the national minimum wage will have had an adverse impact on Outside Delights, as the cost of gardeners will have increased.

Low unemployment in the area will have led to increased wage costs for Outside Delights. |
| Social | The trend towards less structured, more natural gardens will have reduced the amount of gardening work and landscaping work in the area, reducing the total market for Outside Delights. |
| Technological | Competitors have invested in websites incorporating simple garden design software. Customers who engage with this software are more likely to use these competitors for their landscaping instead of Outside Delights. |
| Legal | Changes in the national minimum wage will have had an adverse impact on Outside Delights as the cost of gardeners will have increased.

Changes to health and safety regulations have increased the administrative costs in the business, reducing profitability. |
| Environmental | Customers want to use recycled materials which are harder to handle and so more time consuming to install in landscaping. It may be difficult for Outside Delights to charge a higher price when using these materials.

Less maintenance work is required due to the trend for more natural, less chemically managed gardens, reducing Outside Delights' customer base. |

(iii)

> One of the following actions, or any other sensible suggestion.
> - Invest in a website that includes some simple design software to widen the appeal to new customers.
> - Review the pricing for landscaping jobs using recycled materials, to ensure it is competitive and also profitable.

(b)

Statement	True	False
A partnership agreement contains partners' salaries and commission.	✔	
A partnership must have a partnership agreement in place order to operate.		✔
A limited company is run by the shareholders, on behalf of the directors.		✔
The directors of a limited company must submit a director's report to shareholders as part of the Annual Accounts submitted to Companies House.	✔	

(c) Shareholders are interested in **maximising** their investment, linked to dividends and capital growth.

Shareholders are likely to have a **reasonable appetite for risk.**

Shareholders will normally have **a threshold above** which they are not prepared to go and risk losing their investment.

(d) Cloud accounting can be advantageous for a business to use due to **accounting staff** being able to access and amend real-time financial information.

Task 3

(a) **(i)**

Data is hosted on the organisation's own server.	
Improved sustainability, as more documents are stored electronically.	✔
Data is updated whenever a backup is created.	
Its use relies on the availability of internet access.	✔
Only one user can access a piece of data at any one time.	

(ii)

Data is updated whenever a backup is created.	
Data is backed up automatically to the cloud.	
All stakeholders need to have the cloud accounting software installed on their computers.	✔
Data and information can be accessed remotely from anywhere.	
Its use relies on the availability of internet access.	✔

(b) **(i)**

National Crime Agency (NCA)	
Her Majesty's Revenue & Customs (HMRC)	
Information Commissioner's Office (ICO)	✔
Financial Conduct Authority (FCA)	

(ii)

All data required must be collected at the same time to avoid multiple requests.	
Data can be used for multiple purposes but must not be shared externally with other organisations.	
Data must not be held for any longer than necessary, and a business should be able to justify how long it holds data.	✔
Data must be held on a secure external server to prevent misuse.	
A business must have appropriate processes in place to prove it complies with data protection principles.	✔

(c)

Statement	True	False
Data encryption is installed on a computer system to provide real-time protection against cyberattacks.		✔
A DDoS cyberattack floods an organisation's server with huge numbers of data requests, causing it to freeze up until the attacker's demands are met.	✔	
Browser hijacking changes the user's default home page or search engine allowing the attacker to feed the user with unwanted advertising and popups.	✔	
A firewall will protect the data held by an organisation against internal and external cyberattacks.		✔

(d) **(i)**

Having an in-house IT department with a manager to whom all three IT assistants report.	✔
Passwords that limit access to payroll information to authorised personnel.	
Electronic access logs that record which members of staff have entered different parts of the computer system.	
Limiting certain users' access to the accounting system to read-only.	

(ii) Integrity controls are built into accounting systems to manage and maintain the **accuracy and completeness** of data held by a business.

(e) **(i)**

Statement	Funding source	Appropriate	Not appropriate
To pay the wages of two new delivery drivers the business is considering employing.	Bank loan		✔
To purchase two new delivery vans for the new delivery drivers.	Overdraft		✔
To purchase larger volumes of packaging material for the additional boxes it plans to deliver.	Working capital	✔	

(ii)

Statement	Internal stakeholder	External stakeholder
If Linus and Lucy take out a loan with the bank, the bank will become this type of stakeholder.		✔
The two new delivery drivers that Linus and Lucy plan to employ are this type of stakeholder.	✔	

Task 4

(a) **(i)**

> Providing the information that Edward is asking for about Bolt Supplies Ltd would breach Eli's duty of client confidentiality.
>
> Eli is facing a self-interest threat from Edwards's offer of cash in return for the confidential information.
>
> Eli is facing an intimidation threat from Edward's comment that he 'wonders what George Prento would say if he found out about their arrangement'.
>
> If Eli gives in to the pressure Edward is putting on him, this will compromise Eli's professional judgement, and hence his objectivity.

(ii)

> Eli should refuse to provide the information to Edward as this would be breaching client confidentiality.
>
> Eli should refuse the offer of cash as this is effectively a bribe to get him to do something unethical.
>
> If Eli believes that George Prento is aware of what is going on, he should report the situation to Amelie Desegue.
>
> If he believes that both partners are aware of the situation, he should take advice from his professional accounting body, in this case AAT.
>
> If Eli cannot resolve this ethical conflict, he may have to consider resigning from his position at Prento & Co.

(b) **(i)**

> Libby must make an internal report to the Money Laundering Reporting Officer (MLRO) at Prento & Co detailing her suspicions.
>
> The MLRO will then decide whether to send a suspicious activity report (SAR) to the National Crime Agency.

(ii)

> Libby should not discuss her concerns with the managing director of Wittenbury Travel Ltd as this could result in her being guilty of the money laundering offence of 'tipping off'.

(iii)

> If Wittenbury Travel Ltd is found to be involved in money laundering, and Libby has taken no action in relation to her concerns, she may be guilty of the money laundering offence of 'failure to disclose'. This carries a maximum penalty of five years imprisonment and/or a fine.
>
> Libby may also face disciplinary action by the professional accounting body she is a member of, for example AAT.

Task 5

(a)   (i)

Statement	True	False
Using local staff to work at each festival is an example of social sustainability.	✔	
Using low energy light bulbs is an example economic sustainability.		✔
Encouraging festival goers not to use their own cars is an example of social sustainability.		✔
Including details of these initiatives in its CSR report is likely to have a positive impact on the public perception of Gleewell Ltd.	✔	

(ii)

A public interest duty to protect society as a whole.	
To promote an ethics-based culture within the organisation where they work, and when dealing with clients.	
To ensure the organisation where they work promotes economic sustainability above environmental and social sustainability.	✔

(b)   (i)

An increase in demand for Fye	
A decrease in demand for Fee	✔
An increase in demand for Foe	✔
No change in demand for Fee	

(ii)

A decrease in the price of a Foe	
An increase in the price of a Foe	✔
An increase in the cost of Fye	

(c)

Statement	True	False
The more that a supplier can differentiate its product, the more competitors it will face in the market.		✔
A market with one main supplier who controls most, if not all, of the market is known as a monopoly.	✔	

Task 6

(a) **(i)**

> Answer should cover at least five of the following points, or any other relevant analysis.
> - Sales in October 20-4 were significantly below budget. This could have been due to less marketing, or the sales staff being used to test the website, rather than focusing on selling.
> - Sales in November 20-4 were £27,460 higher than budget.
> - Sales in December 20-4 were significantly (£212,104) higher than budget. This is likely to be due to celebrity endorsements.
> - In November 20-4, internet sales were higher than retail sales, indicating a slight shift in buying patterns.
> - Internet sales in December 20-4 were £211,600 higher than retail sales. This shift in buying pattern could be due to celebrity endorsements online driving up sales.
> - The additional sales in December 20-4, compared with budget, all appear to be due to the increased internet sales.
> - In December 20-4, the business made a healthy profit of £249,689.
> - Cash balances have improved from an overdraft on 30 November 20-4 to a cash balance of £122,500. This is likely to be due to internet sales being settled with payment when the order is placed.

(ii)

> One of the following points.
> - Internet sales may continue to grow strongly as other celebrity endorsements are received.
> - The new website may also contribute to increased sales.
> - The market for luggage made from recycled plastic may grow, as consumers become more aware of the products.

(iii)

> One of the following points.
> - Raw materials costs, which will include recycled plastic, were £258,661 in December 20-4 (32% of total expenses). As more suppliers enter the market, Tyler and Nicole may be able to negotiate lower prices.
> - Delivery costs are 18% of total expenses in December 20-4. The company may benefit from putting all the deliveries through one courier company, reducing the delivery cost per item.

(b)

Sales by product information would identify the least popular lines.	✔
Sales by product information could be used to determine the most profitable items.	
Sales by product information could be used to set production plan.	✔
Sales by product information could be used to update the website.	

(c)

Email	
Telephone call	
Meeting	✔

Task 7

(a) **(i)**

	Transfer	Accept	Reduce	Avoid
The risk to a business's employees who work overseas where there has recently been a large earthquake, and more are expected.				✔
The risk of bad weather causing a tennis final to be postponed.		✔		

(ii)

Risk tolerance	
Risk appetite	✔
Risk threshold	
Risk aversion	

(iii)

Transferral and Avoidance	
Appetite and Tolerance	
Risk and Reward	
Impact and Likelihood	✔

(b)

Finance function information	Sales & Marketing function	Human Resources function	Information Technology function	Board of directors
Details of overdue customer account balances.	✔			
Potential investment strategies for surplus funds.				✔
A letter of resignation from a member of the finance staff.		✔		

(c) **(i)**

Statement	Variety	Veracity	Velocity	Value
Waggys & Whiskers collects data about customers with a wide range of pets, who purchase both online and in-store.	✔			
The data processing function that Waggys & Whiskers has is constantly processing thousands of orders each day across its stores and website.			✔	
Waggys & Whiskers analyses the data it collects to identify trends and anomalies in the purchasing patterns of its customers.		✔		
The analysis Waggys & Whiskers has carried out on its customer data has allowed it to target customers with relevant and attractive discount vouchers.				✔

(ii) The way in which the finance assistant has presented the data helps to ensure that the information is **understandable.**

Answers to practice assessment 2

Task 1

(a)

Statement	True	False
The main rules that govern charities are included in the Companies Act.		✔
Services in the public sector are examples of not-for-profit organisations.	✔	

(b)

Stakeholder	Contribution to the business	Requirements from the business
Shareholders	Capital investment	Profitability
Finance providers	Loaned funds	Regular repayments

(c)

Characteristic	Flat organisational structure	Tall organisational structure	Centralised control	Decentralised control
Authority for decision-making is given to lower levels of management, leading to a more collaborative working environment.				✔
Decisions are imposed on staff rather than allowing the staff to contribute to the decision-making process.			✔	
Information in this type of organisation can pass up and down the chain of command quickly.	✔			

(d) **(i)**

Professional competence and due care	
Objectivity	
Confidentiality	
Professional behaviour	✔

(ii)

Organisation	Can bring disciplinary procedures	Cannot bring disciplinary procedures
AAT	✔	
Gravely Ltd	✔	
HMRC		✔

(e)

Situation	Familiarity threat	Intimidation threat	Advocacy threat	Self-review threat
A client tells its accountant that it may consider changing its accountant if its fees are not reduced by 10%.		✔		
A client has asked its accountant to write an introduction in its brochure for a new share issue, stating what an excellent investment it would be.			✔	
A finance director of a manufacturing business plays golf every weekend with the managing director of one of its main suppliers.	✔			

(f)

Professional competence and due care	
Professional scepticism	✔
Integrity	
Professional behaviour	

(g) **(i)**

The higher costs associated with record keeping and submitting annual returns.	✔
Access to finance, such as bank loans, may be easier than for a sole trader.	
Shareholders' liability for the debts of the business are limited to the amount they have invested in the business.	
Information that is filed at Companies House about the business and its finances can be accessed by anyone.	✔

(ii)

Customers	
Suppliers	
Directors	✔
Banks	

Task 2

(a)

Category	(i) Threat	(ii) Action to reduce the threat
Political	Export tariffs could change, making the products more expensive to overseas customers. As 70% of sales are exported, this could lead to a significant reduction in profits if sales fall.	Increase marketing to improve sales in the UK. Investigate other overseas markets where export tariffs are lower.
	Import tariffs apply, increasing production costs.	To avoid import tariffs, increase use of UK suppliers, where possible.
	Lack of education and training has led to a skills shortage.	Set up an apprenticeship scheme, using government funding, to train the required, skilled labour.
Economic	Changes in tax rates could reduce demand for expensive china, as disposable income will be lower.	Offer several differently priced products, to appeal to different customers.
	Adverse exchange rate movements may reduce the amount of money received by Forestware for sales.	Where possible, invoice in £ sterling. Increase marketing and sales to UK customers.
	Adverse exchange rate movements may result in higher production costs and lower profits.	Increase use of UK suppliers where possible. Negotiate to pay in £ sterling where possible.

Social	Trend to only have one set of tableware reduces the need for a 'best' china set.	Consider increasing product range to appeal to a wider audience who could buy it for everyday use.
		Investigate related markets, eg oven to table cookware, to broaden product range.
	China patterns are not being updated to reflect modern homeware trends.	Update patterns to reflect modern tableware trends.

(iii)

One of:

Environmental

Technological

Legal

(b)

Statement	Advantage
Automation	Improved data integrity
Machine learning	Complex data can be analysed
Qualified electronic signature	Quick and efficient validation of parties involved
Blockchain	Encryption of data, so only authorised users can access it

(c)

Statement	True	False
A partnership must cease to operate when a partner retires.		✔
Goodwill in a partnership is defined as the difference between the value of a business as a whole and the net value of its assets.		✔

(d) Financial statements of limited companies **must** be prepared under International Accounting Standards. Directors of large, limited companies **must** ensure the financial statements are audited.

Task 3

(a)

Statement	True	False
A business owner who breaches data protection legislation may face a prison sentence.		✔
A data subject can request for data a business holds about them to be destroyed at any point.	✔	
Once a business has used personal data for the purpose it was collected, it should delete it immediately.	✔	
In the UK the Information Commissioner's Office is the body that regulates and enforces GDPR.	✔	

(b)

The accounting system is automatically updated each time a piece of data is added.	✔
The accounting system is held on the organisation's server and backed up to the cloud at predefined intervals.	
The accounting system will incorporate an element of Artificial Intelligence (AI), which means that staff will not need to be trained in how to use it.	
Cloud accounting will increase the IT costs of the business and reduce the software costs.	
Access to cloud accounting relies on users having internet access and appropriate software installed on their computers.	✔

(c)   (i)

Statement	Inseparability	Perishability	Intangibility	Variability
The service has to be used as it is provided as any unused service cannot be stored for future use.		✔		
The service will be specifically designed to meet the needs of the individual customer or client.				✔
The provision and consumption of the service happen at the same time.	✔			
The service is not generally a physical product.			✔	

(ii)   This demonstrates that Sasha's business benefits from **defined responsibilities for staff members.**

(d)

Part of a computer application designed to manage and maintain the completeness and accuracy of data.	Integrity controls
A barrier that sits between a business's internal computer network and the public internet.	Firewall
Software that runs in the background and provides real-time protection to a business's computer system again cyberattacks.	Anti-virus software

(e)

	Spyware	DDoS	Ransomware	Malware
The general term for malicious software, often inserted into computer via phishing emails, that can introduce viruses, keyloggers, spyware, worms, or ransomware.				✔
This allows the attacker to watch the operations of the business without being seen by the user.	✔			
A cyberattack that locks the user out of their information system and makes demands, usually money, to prevent further disruption.			✔	

Task 4

(a) (i)

> Riley's professional competence and due care is threatened in this situation as he does not currently have sufficient knowledge and experience to complete the work unsupervised. This means that there may be a risk he will not produce the information to a satisfactory standard.
>
> There is also a self-interest threat to Riley's objectivity, as the finance director has said how well he carries out the work will affect his pay review.

(ii)

> Any two of the following:
>
> • Explain to the finance director that he will need advice, or training, on how to complete the depreciation information.
>
> • Ensure he has sufficient time to complete the work.
>
> • Ensure that his work is reviewed before it is provided to the auditors.
>
> • Explain to the finance director that he doesn't want to take on work beyond his competency just to ensure he gets a pay rise.

(b) (i)

> Money laundering is a criminal activity that moves illegally acquired money through financial systems so that it appears to have been legally acquired.

(ii)

> 1. Placement
>
> 2. Layering
>
> 3. Integration

(iii)

> Integration is the final stage of the money laundering process which integrates illegal funds back into the legitimate financial system, often by investing in property and other legitimate assets.

Task 5

(a) **(i)**

Corporate sustainability reporting	
Critical social responsibility	
Corporate social responsibility	✔
Corporate sustainable responsibility	

(ii)

Evidence	Economic responsibility	Social responsibility	Environmental responsibility
Where possible, Cyrus & Co sources goods and services from local suppliers.	✔		
The standard business email signature for all staff at Cyrus & Co includes the words: 'Think before you print! Do you need to print this email?'			✔
Cyrus & Co encourages its staff to take part in local charitable activities and provides them with time off work, or financial support, to do so.		✔	

(iii)

Statement	True	False
Accountants in practice must ensure that the firm they work for upholds sustainability and sustainable development, but this duty does not extend to ensuring their clients do the same.		✔

(b) **(i)**

Increase in the cost of production labour	✔
Increase in the price of the normal good	
Decrease in the VAT charged on the sale of the normal good	
Decrease in the price of the normal good	

(ii)

Statement	True	False
Substitute products are those which consumers will buy regardless of whether their income changes.		✔
Normal goods are those for which demand increases when income increases, and goes down if income decreases.	✔	
Cheaper goods for which demand generally decreases as income rises are known as necessity goods.		✔
If the price of a normal good decreases, demand for a complementary good will generally increase.	✔	

Task 6

(a)   (i)

> The dashboard uses visual representations of information, such as graphs and charts, to help non-financial managers interpret and understand financial information more easily. It is often clearer than using tables, and may make it easier to determine trends and relationships between data.

(ii)

> Answer should include at least three of the points below, or any other relevant point.
>
> - Revenue from other contracts has fallen from £41,600 in April 20-8 to £38,400 in June 20-8. If this trend continues, the profitability of the company is likely to be affected.
> - Half the 49-seaters are still using petrol, which has a higher cost per passenger mile than the electric 49 seaters.
> - Outstanding receivables at the end of June 20-8 are £145,024 (£66,880 + £38,400 + £6,624 + £33,120). The company offers credit of 30 days, but at the end of June 20-8, over 27% ((£6,624 + £33,120) /£145,024) of the receivables are overdue.
> - The company is heavily reliant on contract revenue from schools. In June 20-8, nearly 42% ((£66,880 / (£66,880 + £38,400 + £54,600)) of revenue was from school contracts. The schools' contracts are due to be awarded in July 20-8, and the company could face significant financial difficulties if some, or all, of this revenue is lost.
> - Drivers' costs as a percentage of revenue for contracts have increased in May and June 20-8. This may be due to one-off events, such as agency cover for staff illness. If it is a permanent increase, profitability may be permanently reduced.

(iii)

> One of the following points:
> - Concentrate on ad hoc hires as this market is growing – sales in June 20-8 compared with April 20-8 were up by 38% (£54,600 / £39,600). These customers do not require credit.
> - The smaller, hybrid vehicles are cheaper to run and earn a profit of £0.07 per passenger mile, compared with £0.03 for the petrol 49-seater, and £0.05 for the electric 49-seater. Further investment in this type of vehicle could improve profitability.

(iv)

> One of the following points, or any other sensible suggestion:
> - Profit/loss per the month compared with budget
> - Breakdown of expenses for the month
> - Cash and bank balances

(b)

The most recent set of financial statements	✔
Access to the accounting software, including the dashboard	
Copies of all drivers' employment contracts	
Business forecasts, incorporating the new vehicles	✔

(c)

Email	✔
Social media posts	
Posters on coaches	

Task 7

(a)   (i)

Velocity	✔
Variability	
Volume	✔
Valid	

(ii)

Statement	Social data	Machine data	Transactional data
Data from satellite tracking that shows the routes and timings of deliveries made by a courier.		✔	
The number, and timing, of views of an organisation's promotional video on YouTube.	✔		
Data about products, prices, and the timing of customer purchases, recorded at a supermarket checkout.			✔

(b)   (i)

Statement	True	False
A business that pays for insurance on the inventory held in its warehouse against fire is an example of risk avoidance.		✔
Risk averse stakeholders will be willing to accept a lower return in order to minimise the risk they face.	✔	
The risk to a business of failing to maintain health and safety standards in its factories overseas is an example of reputational risk.	✔	
A new supplier entering the market for a product at a lower price is an example of a strategic risk.	✔	

(ii)

The risk of over-reliance on a key member of production staff.	
The risk of fraudulent transactions going undetected in the payroll system.	
A shortage of labour to work in the production department of a business.	✔
The risk that defective products go unnoticed by the quality assurance department.	

(c)

The fact that Frieda extracts the information about overtime hours worked from the clocking in and out system will help to ensure that the information is **accurate**.
Presenting the information to the production manager as a graph helps to ensure that the information is **understandable**.

Answers to practice assessment 3

Task 1

(a)

Statement	True	False
A sole trader must make an annual return to Companies House.		✔
If a partnership is formed without a partnership agreement, the partnership will be governed by the Partnership Act.	✔	

(b) **(i)**

Administrative staff	
Bakers	
Sasha Briars	✔
Local authority	

(ii)

Administrative staff	
Bakers	
Cake decorators	✔
Local authority	

(iii)

The bank	
Sasha Briars	✔
Local authority	
The Government	

(c)

Co-operation	✔
Defined structure	✔
Profitability targets	
Goal congruence	✔
Limited liability	

(d) **(i)**

Statement	True	False
In addition to being a fundamental ethical principle, confidentiality is also a legal obligation.	✔	

(ii)

Situation	Can be disclosed	Cannot be disclosed
A request from a local builder's merchants for financial information about a client who has asked to buy from them on credit terms.		✔
Information about a client for whom the accountant ceased working three years ago.		✔
The accountant has been asked to provide documents about a client as part of an ongoing court case.	✔	
AAT is conducting a disciplinary inquiry into one of the partners in the accounting practice for which the accountant works.	✔	

(e) Jon Joffrey's request is **an advocacy threat** to Deidra's fundamental ethical principle of **objectivity**.

(f)

Providing fair treatment, decent wages, and good working conditions for all employees	
Appropriate use of social media	
Paying suppliers a fair price and on time	
Ensuring an annual dividend is paid to shareholders	✔

(g)

Statement	True	False
Decentralised control leads to a more collaborative working environment.	✔	
An organisation with a number of new products being developed will benefit from a matrix structure.	✔	
A manager in a smaller organisation is likely to have a narrower span of control.		✔
A business with separate departments for finance, sales, production, distribution, and human resources, is likely to have a functional structure.	✔	

Task 2

(a)

Category	(i) Threat	(ii) Action to reduce the threat
Social	Customers are looking for non-dairy alternatives to traditional milk-based milkshakes. Drinks using oat and soya milk are becoming increasingly popular, reducing the market for dairy milkshakes.	Consider using the organic oats currently being grown on the farm to make a non-dairy oat milk product.
	Health-conscious consumers are likely to prefer lower sugar drinks, so may choose not to buy Molly's Milkshakes.	Promote the health benefits of drinking milk in marketing campaigns. Reduce the amount of sugar in the product.
Legal	The Government's 'sugar tax' makes the milkshakes more expensive, which customers may not be willing to pay.	Reformulate the recipes to reduce the amount of sugar used.
	New legislation for improved labelling of ingredients and nutritional value must be complied with as failure to do so may result in a fine, and/or damage to the business's reputation.	The business should fully investigate the new legislation, and take expert advice, if necessary, to ensure all its products are correctly labelled.
Environmental	Customers may choose to buy products with packaging that is better for the environment.	Investigate more environmentally friendly packaging, such as recyclable bottles made from recycled plastic.
	Milk is transported to the production plant, with some of the farms being over 50 miles away.	Consider sourcing more milk from local farms, so that less transport is required, thereby reducing the carbon footprint of the product.

(iii)

One of:

Political
Economic
Technological

(b) When a partner joins a partnership, **all** of the partners must agree to the change.

Goodwill must be determined when a **partner retires from, or joins,** the partnership.

(c)

Statement	True	False
All limited companies are required to have an Articles of Association.	✔	
All financial statements of limited companies must include notes to the accounts.	✔	

(d)

Protection against hacking	✔
Forecasting future data accurately	
Reducing costs and improving efficiency of record keeping	✔
Lower IT costs	

Task 3

(a)

Advantage	Artificial Intelligence (AI)	Electronic document filing	Block-chain	Data analytics
Provides certainty about the integrity of data by protecting against unauthorised access.			✔	
Identifies anomalies in data and diagnoses why they may have occurred.				✔
Complex data can be analysed to form the basis of future decision-making.	✔			
Protects documents and business records against fire or flood.		✔		

(b)   **(i)**

Situation	Keylogging	Phishing
Ramona has received an email telling her to click on the link to pay an overdue invoice.		✔
The anti-virus software at Rolo Ltd has picked up an instance of malware that is recording what Ramona is typing into her computer.	✔	

(ii)

Corruption or misuse of customer information by a third party	✔
Increased inventory insurance costs	
Operational risk of the loss of key staff	
Temporary or permanent IT system failure	✔

(c) **(i)** Once a business has finished using personal data it should **destroy the data in a secure manner**.

(ii)

	True	False
There is no maximum limit on the fine that can be imposed for breaches of data protection principles.		✔
Data should be used only for the explicit purpose for which it was given.	✔	
It is up to the data subject to ensure that the data an organisation holds about them is accurate and up-to-date.		✔

(d) **(i)**

Ffion would be able to extend her business to offer services internationally.	
The cloud accounting system could link to the business's bank account and post some of the transactions automatically.	✔
Ffion would no longer need to maintain her spreadsheet accounting system.	✔
Ffion would no longer need to employ the bookkeeper as the system will prepare the VAT Returns and annual accounts, automatically.	
Ffion will need to have the same cloud accounting software as the bookkeeper uses.	
The bookkeeper would be able to access the accounting system in real-time.	✔

(ii)

	True	False
Ffion is the only stakeholder in the business.		✔
Because the business offers a service to its customers, it is easier to have a standard price list.		✔
The majority of Ffion's expenses will be staff costs.	✔	

Task 4

(a)

> It is not acceptable for Suranne to invest in Finleys Ltd.
>
> This is a **self-interest threat** to Charlie's fundamental ethical principle of **objectivity**. As a professional accountant he should not have an interest, ie own shares or have loans, either directly, or indirectly, in a client he works for.
>
> If Suranne does invest in Finleys Ltd, the only acceptable safeguard to address this threat would be for Charlie to stop providing accounting services to the business.

(b)

> Keisha's professional competence and due care will be most threatened as her technical competence is unlikely to be up-to-date.
>
> Keisha should carry out some relevant continuing professional development to ensure she is technically up-to-date.

(c)　**(i)**

> It is unusual for a business to pay such large sums of cash for supplies. This may indicate that the cash has been illegally obtained.
>
> If this is the case, it would mean that, by accepting the cash payments, Inkwell Ltd may also be guilty of money laundering.
>
> George should discuss his concerns with the financial controller. However, he will have to be careful about how he raises the matter as the managing director of Inkwell Ltd is a shareholder of Kazamm Ltd.
>
> As George does not work in the regulated sector, Inkwell Ltd will not have a Money Laundering Reporting Officer (MLRO), so he will have to report his suspicions to the National Crime Agency (NCA) using suspicious activity report (SAR).

Task 5

(a)   (i)

Organisational policy	Economic/ Financial responsibility	Social responsibility	Environmental responsibility
Bamberoli Ltd has a policy to match any charitable fundraising carried out by members of staff, up to a maximum of £500 per staff member per year.		✔	
Pandaworks Ltd manufactures toilet tissue. It has undertaken to plant a tree for every pack of its product that is sold.			✔
Greener Groundwork Ltd is an environmentally friendly landscape gardening business. All projects it tenders for are costed in detail and include a built-in 25% profit margin.	✔		

(ii)

Sustainable development meets the needs of the present without **compromising the ability of future generations to meet their own needs**.
Professional accountants should **promote sustainable practices in their workplace**.

(b)   (i)

The point where the price and the cost of a normal good are equal.	
All competitors in the market sell a product for the same price.	
The price at which supply and demand are equal.	✔
There is a monopoly in the market, so the price remains unchanged to all customers.	

(ii)

Statement	True	False
A change in price of a good or service will result in a shift along the demand curve.	✔	
The price mechanism only works to find the equilibrium price for necessity goods.		✔
A decrease in the number of buyers in the market for a product will make the market more competitive.	✔	
Set up costs are likely to be more of a barrier to entry for Paulette who is setting up as a bookkeeper than for Lionel who is setting up a café and cake-making business.		✔

Task 6

(a)   (i)

Performance to December 20-2
- Sales revenues decreased from July to October 20-2, before improving in November and December 20-2.
- Revenue for Bristol is the highest in all months except September and October.
- The drop in revenue for Bristol in September and October was probably due to Tonya's absence.
- Sales at the Birmingham and Hereford branches show steady growth in the period, so these sales managers are performing well.
- Sales revenue for both Worcester and Stratford-upon-Avon branches is reducing each month. This could be due to reduced sales staff, as these branches found it difficult to replace staff when they left.
- Sales of people carriers, estate cars and sports utility vehicles have remained fairly constant over the six months.
- The highest selling products in each of the months are medium family cars and small hatchbacks.
- The fewest number of cars sold in a month was in October 20-2, resulting in October recording the lowest monthly revenue.
- The fall in sales of medium family cars in September and October has led to reduced revenue in these months. This may be due to an amended pricing policy introduced by the Bristol sales manager whilst Tonya was off work.

Expected performance for January 20-3
- New sales staff have been recruited for Stratford-Upon-Avon and Worcester, so sales in these branches are likely to increase once they are fully trained.
- Bristol is likely to continue to be the highest performing branch.
- Sales of small hatchbacks and medium family cars are increasing and may continue to do so.

(ii)

> One of the following points:
>
> • Profit/loss per the location per month
>
> • Budgeted vs actual profit or sales per location per month

(b)

Matter	Email	Meeting	Telephone
Tonya wants to amend the basic salary and bonus scheme, to make it more appealing to the salespeople. The views of some of the current sales team would be useful.		✔	
Tonya would like to open a new branch in Leicester and wants to inform current staff members of the job description, as they may wish to apply for the sales manager role.	✔		

Task 7

(a) **(i)**

Finance function requirement	Production function	Human Resources function	Information Technology function	Distribution function
Costs and schedule for servicing delivery vehicles.				✔
Number of units manufactured by staff on piecework pay.	✔			
Salaries for new employees.		✔		

(ii)

> Milos's suggestion to present the information using graphs and charts would help to ensure that the information is **understandable**.

> The fact that Milos may have to rush to complete the work on time means that the information may not be **accurate**.

(b) **(i)**

Risk tolerance	—
Risk appetite	
Risk threshold	✔
Risk aversion	

(ii)

	Transfer	Accept	Reduce	Avoid
A chemical business that subcontracts the disposal of hazardous waste to an expert waste management company.	✔			
A website business that carries out regular staff training on the data protection principles included in GDPR.			✔	

(c)

Statement	True	False
One of the advantages to Brilliant Burgers of collecting large amounts of data about its customers is that it can establish trends in purchasing and patterns of behaviour.	✔	
Because customers have chosen to sign up for the loyalty scheme, Brilliant Burgers can share the customer data with the delivery companies that it uses.		✔
The data that Brilliant Burgers is collecting will allow it to analyse its market share.		✔
Proper analysis of the data collected by Brilliant Burgers will help the business to decide where to open further branches.	✔	

for your notes

for your notes

for your notes

for your notes

for your notes

for your notes

for your notes